FOREVER NATURAL

How to Excel in Sports Drug-Free

by
Dave Tuttle

Copyright © 1990

Library of Congress Card Catalog Number: 90-80473
International Standard Book Number: 0-9625740-0-7

Second Printing

Published by:

Iron Books
P.O. Box 2307
Venice, California 90294

Printed in the United States of America

TABLE OF CONTENTS

FIGURES AND TABLES

i

ACKNOWLEDGEMENTS

Many people have made contributions to this book through their thoughtful suggestions and support. I would first like to thank Eric Sternlicht, Ph.D., who was my principal technical advisor. Eric's assistance helped guide me through the detailed research that was needed to make this book a reality.

Several other people reviewed this book prior to its publication. These individuals have provided me with a great number of observations and comments, for which I am most grateful. In alphabetical order, they are: Chris Aceto, Steve Holman, John Hutson, Jill Leitz, Sid Levee, Jerry Robinson, Garrett Smith and Ken Taylor.

I would also like to thank my parents, who provided me with the patience, perseverance and goal orientation that have helped me make the natural commitment to my sport.

PREFACE

During my years as a competitive athlete I have seen many enthusiastic people looking for that magic pill that will somehow make *the* difference in their athletic performance. This search for a shortcut to success frequently leads them to steroids and other chemicals. Recently, there has also been a rise in steroid use by teenage men, many of whom don't compete in sports but who take steroids to increase their "attractiveness" and self-esteem without any intention of ever participating in athletics.

These rationales for drug use are unfortunate. They hurt the individuals taking the chemicals as well as those who compete with them. It is my hope that this book will show those persons considering performance-enhancing drugs that these "sports medicines" are full of physical and psychological health risks that make the chemical path to athletic greatness a dangerous and, in the long term, counterproductive effort. Sports should help us to lead a full, healthy and balanced life. Drug use weakens the foundations for this pursuit.

My goal in writing this book is to demonstrate that these performance-enhancing agents are not even needed to succeed in sports. There is no reason why a person who follows the guidelines in this book for nutrition, recuperation and training technique cannot achieve an athletic body that is among the finest around without resorting to chemical assistance. This is what I seek for myself, and what I feel others seek as well: to have muscular, fit bodies that we can take pride in and enjoy for the rest of our lives—bodies that will let us enjoy the pleasure of sports and be healthy as well.

Forever Natural contains a summary of the latest research on nutrition and sports performance, as well as many of the findings I have learned during my years as a competitive athlete. By necessity I have had to simplify much of the scientific information contained in these pages. The book begins with a discussion of the reasons some athletes are tempted to use drugs. A brief history of sports is also included to show how sports thrived for many years without the scourge of drug abuse. Surely this healthy environment for sports competition can exist again—once we recognize the problem and deal with the root causes of why athletes take these health-threatening drugs.

A complete chapter is devoted to the physiology of muscular development. This chapter provides you with background information that will help you to understand how your body functions, and, as such, is rather technical. If you like, you can skip this chapter and read the chapters on nutrition and training technique first. Many of the recommendations in these latter chapters, however, are based on the information contained in the physiology chapter, so if you do skip it you'll need to accept these recommendations without knowing the underlying reasons for them. It depends on your personal preference.

Next there is a chapter discussing the characteristics of steroids and growth-hormone supplements. This chapter explains the short-term benefits of drug use as well as the long-term impacts associated with it. The information on benefits is included so that natural athletes can understand why some of their competitors are tempted to use drugs. (Those already on drugs know the short-term benefits—that's why they use them!) It is hoped that this information, along with the detailed facts on the dangers of drug abuse, will help natural athletes convince their more short-sighted fellow competitors to stop using drugs. After all, the elimination of steroids and growth hormone from athletic competition will take place only after every individual in-volved has made his or her personal decision not to use them. It is my sincere hope that this book will help.

Following this discussion are four chapters on diet and nutrition. This topic has received the greatest emphasis in the book because proper nutrition is absolutely essential for the natural athlete in his or her quest for optimal sports performance. While everyone benefits from sound nutrition, it is the main tool that natural athletes have available to them to rise to the top of their sports. Information is given on the three macronutrients—protein, carbohydrate and fat—as well as all of the micronutrients. There is also a discussion on so-called ergogenic aids, which are claimed to have performance-enhancing benefits. Techniques for controlling body weight are reviewed as well. Following this theoretical information are two "application" chapters: Tips for Home-Cooked Meals and Tips for Eating Out. The book therefore provides the theory of nutrition and all the day-to-day information you will need to apply this theory in real life.

Next there are two chapters devoted to training technique. Even with proper nutrition, no natural athlete can excel without utilizing the right training techniques. Nowadays most athletes lift weights to gain the strength (and frequently the muscle mass) needed to win in their respective sports. The book focuses on the ways you can get the most benefit from this progressive-resistance training. Included in this discussion are the eight training principles fundamental to success, as well as detailed descriptions on warming up, progressive-resistance training, isometrics, stretching, aerobic exercise, rest and recuperation. This information complements the chapters on nutrition to form a complete whole that will allow natural athletes to achieve their goals without resorting to dangerous drugs.

The book concludes with a chapter on balancing your life. This is an element of lifelong fitness that is not always considered. People who let one part of their lives (be it work or exercise) dominate to the detriment of other parts usually find their lives less fulfilling than people who draw strength from a variety of pursuits. This idea is explored, and several suggestions for achieving balance are offered.

All the different elements of fitness noted above are part of an integrated system for living naturally. Just as balancing your life's activities is a crucial part of a healthy lifestyle, so too are nutrition, exercise and recuperation the keys to balanced body development. This book provides you with all you need to know to lead a natural and physically healthy life. The rest is up to you!

I hope you find reading this book as interesting as it has been for me to write it. In good health,

Dave Tuttle

WARNING

While exercise can be very beneficial, it can also result in injury—especially if you are not in good physical condition. Always consult with your physician before beginning any program of weight training or exercise. If you start exercising and feel any strain or pain, stop immediately and consult your physician.

Also, remember to follow exercise instructions carefully. Since this book does not deal with the specifics of individual exercises, you are strongly urged to consult other books or a competent personal trainer before performing all exercises. Always start with very light weights and exercise at your own pace. Remember, you can't train and grow if you're injured. Respect your body and it will give you the greatest rewards it is capable of.

CHAPTER ONE

The Natural Commitment

Steroids have been in the news a lot lately. Sports pages are filled with disclosures about Olympic athletes and professional football players who have used these "performance-enhancing" drugs to win. There has even been disturbing news about the rise in steroid use by teenagers, many of whom don't participate in varsity athletic programs. At times it seems like drugs are everywhere—a regrettable yet real fact of life that athletes just have to tolerate.

There's no reason to accept this state of affairs. Steroid use can and in time will be eliminated. Every year better methods are being developed to catch athletes who try to beat their competitors with a chemical helping hand. Increased vigilance and the possible imposition of year-round random testing will make drug use increasingly difficult and unacceptable. These tests and regulations, which are improving all the time, will catch the cheaters and put them in their place.

By casting drugs aside and seeking a scientifically-based natural route for stimulating your body's growth and performance, natural athletes like you will be able to achieve all that someone relying on drugs could achieve. And, since your performance will not be tied to some artificial chemical, you will be able to lead a long and healthy life that will offer you the greatest rewards of sport achievement.

Achieving Your Goals Naturally

George Eiferman, the 1948 Mr. America and 1962 Mr. Universe, said it well when he noted:

> Probably the greatest discovery anyone can make is that we can change our life for the better, by changing our immature, negative attitudes to MATURE, constructive attitudes. We live in the direction of our thought patterns. Let's have our attitudes work for us instead of against us.

Much of the current use of steroids, especially among teens, is caused by the feeling that they can't control their lives. These feelings of fatalism stem from a lack of confidence in their ability to achieve their goals naturally. "If I've been dealt this hand", they feel, "this limits my potential and sets my constraints. There are only so many cards in the deck. If I really want to make that major leap forward so I can have a really impressive body and attract that special someone I'll have to use drugs. And the more the better!"

This line of thinking can lead to major drug abuse. In an attempt to outdo their peers and take the easy way out, these persons wind up taking higher dosages than even professional athletes. If the gains don't come quickly enough, they may take two or three different drugs at a time, creating potential for negative interactions and intensified organ damage. The results can be tragic.

By taking a shortcut to the image they seek, these athletes put unnecessary strains on their bodies and potentially damage themselves physically and emotionally. Drugs can also give you a false sense of your potential, pushing you to overtrain to the point of injury. While the body has amazing recuperative powers, too much substance abuse will inevitably lead to damage. In the real world, there is no free lunch. Never has been, never will. Everything has its price. If someone tells you steroids are the answer, they are either misinformed or selling drugs for a profit. Don't be fooled!

The feeling that you can control your life leads to a sense of direction and positive aggression. You can determine the way you want to run your life and select the means for doing so. This positive mental energy will literally help make things happen.

Many years ago a poem titled *Energy* appeared in a magazine. The author was uncredited. This poem sums up the idea of positive energy quite well.

Energy, heated by emotion,
charged with will,
directed by the intellect,
moves with confidence and pride
like an ambassador on an important mission.
It manifests itself in conscious action,
full of feeling, content and purpose,
which must be fulfilled
in accordance with its impulses.

No accomplishment in the real world is without cost. If something is worthwhile, hard work and effort will be needed to achieve it. After all, if sport achievement or anything else were easy, wouldn't everyone do it? And that would likely take most of the satisfaction and enjoyment away from it. If you have a direction to your life, you will find it fuller and more complete. There will also be greater contentment with your current situation in life, since you know that your path is leading somewhere. The hassles of the present then become part of a transition to a better and more fruitful future. From this evolves a confidence about your chosen direction, and a greater sense that you will achieve your goals regardless of the time involved.

This sense of confidence is essential to natural athletes, who need to patiently persevere while others, who are just as genetically gifted but use drugs, catapult ahead of them in size and strength "progress". It helps to know that their "progress" comes from a bottle and isn't the real thing. Yet in the absence of a firm commitment to your sport and the confidence that you will eventually reach your goals, this may not be much of a consolation. You need to keep a long range viewpoint that gives you the strength to wait, so you won't be tempted to take drugs.

The Ups and Downs of Steroids

When many people start to train for a sport they are encouraged by coaches and so-called friends to take steroids. Peer pressure and the athlete's desire for acceptance may be strong motivational factors. The person may also be told that taking drugs is the ONLY way to make gains, and that an athlete must win at all costs. The lure of money may even be dangled in front of them, since they will be told that "all" professional athletes use drugs.

These arguments can be very tempting at the beginning. Yet over time you will see how people go through cycles and change. In three or four months a drug-using bodybuilder might gain 15 pounds and have thinner skin and more visible muscles to boot. A sprinter might make remarkable increases in speed. This provides for an immediate gratification of their training goals. Yet a year later, after they are "off the juice" for some time, these athletes are right back where they started, looking (or running) like mere shadows of their former selves. Someone pulled the plug. After a while, you will observe this happening with lots of athletes—their weights rising and falling like the tide, in extreme cases even stretching their skin and causing permanent scars.

Steroids can also cause major mood swings in users—turning them into irritable grouches who are always on a very short fuse. One drug-abuser even violently confronted the driver of a car ahead of him when that driver had the audacity to stop at a yellow light. How dare he do such an unforgivable act! Fights at the gym have started over the stupidest topics or perceived insults. Yet while difficult for those around them, drug-abusing athletes can feel a definite high from steroids, pumping their minds full of images of superheroes. In fact, this psychoactive element of the drug is part of the reason it works, since if your mind feels you're a superhero, your strength can actually increase. After all, what's a mere 300-pound bench press to a Man or Woman of Steel?

Of course, the opposite side of the coin becomes apparent when the drug is discontinued. Like an addict who has run out of coke, major negative mood swings can take place. (Worse for some people than others, to be sure.) The former Superhero now feels like Superwimp. Weights that were once easy are now major challenges or not even possible. The psychological crutch is gone. Some athletes have given up sports entirely or even committed suicide when they stopped using steroids. The thought of going back to the gym 15 or 20 pounds lighter was too intolerable for them to imagine. What were they going to tell everyone—that they caught a mean flu? The drug-induced high is often replaced by a depression that can impact their social lives and work as well. Once you've seen this cycle happen to others, you will make a firm resolution to stay forever natural.

While some people at the gym are going through these mega-mood swings, you continue pushing along, making slow but steady progress toward your athletic goals. Yet since your gains are natural, they don't go away. Without reliance on a drug, your body makes gradual yet continual progress that in the long term outpaces the drug-abusing athlete, who, although it may take years, will eventually

4

have to give up his steroid use when his body protests too much. Some professional bodybuilders have lost 50 pounds when they quit their habits. This senseless abuse of your biological support system has no place in the life of anyone interested in his or her long-term health.

Remember the fable about the tortoise and the hare? The hare took off in a dash, of course, while the tortoise slowly but surely made constant progress. We all know who won that race. The same is true in the race of life. Those who try to jump ahead and make progress through drug-induced spurts may be ahead at the halfway line, but inevitably they will fall behind the ever-increasing gains of the natural athlete. Final victory will be ours!

A positive mental headset is essential. "I'm going to live to be 100," you should think. True, not everyone will reach that ripe old age, but it's essential to think in the long term. This headset leads to lengthened horizons, which is a very liberating feeling. "I'm 35 now—that means I've got 65 years to go. That's a lot more hills to climb and a lot more time to succeed at the goals I have set for myself. So what if it takes a few more years to excel drug-free? I've got all the time I need!"

This is not to say that life is all peaches and cream. There are inevitable setbacks that throw us for a loop and force us to retrench and set new directions. What matters is how you react to the setback. You need to lick your wounds and move on, accepting the setbacks without lingering regrets or remorse. Learn and grow from them. By dwelling on the negative, you occupy your mind and keep positive thoughts from coming in. This negativity can be a trap.

We have all known people who rise above adversity and still keep their confidence and self-esteem. Persons of all ages become afflicted with diseases or are handicapped, perhaps because of a car accident. Yet the reaction to this distress varies with the individual. Some seem to wallow in their own misery, looking for sympathy or pity. Others, confronted with the exact same illness or handicap, maintain their grip on life and, if anything, find new interests and reasons to live. There is a bodybuilder in Arizona who went blind in his 30s. Instead of treating it like the end of his life, he intensified his training and is now a frequent competitor and guest poser, enjoying his life to the fullest. Positive energy truly makes the difference.

Negativity about physical growth can even affect the development of particular bodyparts. If you say to yourself "these calves won't grow," they won't. The mind effectively blocks the muscle's development by sending fewer signals to that muscle during exercise and diverting its limited mental energy to another part of the body. The bodypart will therefore tire more quickly, or seem to have less strength. The result of this negativity will be reduced benefit from resistance training and an unbalanced physique. At the same time, positive feedback from friends or unusually rapid growth in a certain muscle can cause the athlete to give too much priority to a bodypart, resulting in a similar lack of proportion.

Sometimes we create monsters in our minds. Faced with a daunting task, we invent obstacles or imagine a series of difficult steps that need to be surmounted before we reach our objective. These monstrous thoughts produce stress, which can make the goal seem even more insurmountable. Of course, there are hoops to jump through and frustrations in the pursuit of any goal. Yet while a recognition of the potential problems ahead is healthy, concentrating on them to the point that they make the goal seem unreachable (or not worth the effort) can undermine positive action and progress.

These side-tracking emotions can be devastating for the natural athlete. The way to achieve a top-level physique or optimal perform- ance in your sport is through total mental concentration. You need to focus all of your positive energy on the particular movement you are doing at that moment. Some persons go into a meditative "training trance" where they clear all the extraneous thoughts from their mind and totally concentrate on the present. Others achieve this focus by visualizing the movement in their mind and thinking only of that visualization for the entire time they're training. This is true for any sport, from running and swimming to powerlifting. Total concentra- tion will allow you to direct your maximum mental energy to the task at hand, stimulating the greatest amount of muscle growth. If your mind is distracted by negative thoughts, or if your eye is constantly on the clock because you might be late for work or whatever, these distractions will reduce the intensity of your workout and keep you from achieving your true potential.

Athletes, by their very natures, are impatient. They not only want it all, they want it NOW. This need for immediate gratification is reinforced in our culture, with its demands for instant microwave dinners and the like. Yet sport is not an activity in which you become an overnight sensation. Even those athletes who pop onto the national scene out of nowhere have trained for many years to get where they are. Body development is a slow and deliberate process that takes a long time. This is a fact of life for every sport.

You need to adopt an attitude that accepts how long it takes to achieve sport excellence. This recognition allows you to fight against the inevitable down periods when gains seem to be too slow or nonexistent. Rome wasn't built in a day, and neither will your body be. But if you hold onto a positive attitude, and tie that to a drive that says "I won't give up until I'm satisfied," you will achieve your goals just as surely as the sun rising in the morning. Steroids will not be necessary.

Sometimes there is social and peer pressure to take drugs. People who have made major visible gains, and are therefore role models, may use them. Friends may also urge you to "just try" them, and may imply that you're chicken if you don't go along. The temptations are real. Yet the decision to give in to the temptations is a personal one, and each person has control of his or her personal life.

Steroids can also be counterproductive in the long run because you may wind up relying on them, making gains "the easy way" and slacking off on the intensity of your workouts. After all, if you're growing, that's good enough, right? The problem with this headset is that drug use by its very nature is temporary. No one can stay on drugs forever. It's better to make your gains slowly but surely than to jump-start and then lose them in the end.

Insecurity can also play a role in a person's decision to use steroids. Feelings of insecurity keep you from having confidence about yourself, so you feel that your ideas and opinions are less valid than other people's. This insecurity holds back your potential, for it is only when a person is confident of his or her abilities that he/she can truly rise above the crowd and be a true achiever. This is particularly true in individual sports like bodybuilding, gymnastics or track, where you are out there performing on your own. Don't let others hold you back!

The Chemical Age of Athletics

One day we will look back on the 1970s and 1980s as the Chemical Age in Athletics. It was during this period that steroid use went from being an occasional occurrence by a few professional athletes to a common practice by many persons competing in sports and lots of other people as well. Yet history will show that people learned through hard experience the hazards of steroid abuse, and that drug use declined as quickly as it rose in popularity. It may sound unusual to talk in this way, since we are still in this Chemical Age, but there is an analogy in agriculture that is very revealing.

7

Starting a bit earlier, in the 1950s and 1960s, agriculture entered its own Chemical Age. People schooled in chemical ways "knew" that fertilizers, pesticides and herbicides were absolutely necessary for things to grow to their maximum potential. Of course, they felt there were no problems associated with use of these chemicals. So for a few decades people went on blithely using them, secure in their feelings that this was not only the best way to do things, but the only possible way as well.

In time, of course, the dangers of pesticides, herbicides and fertilizers became known. By the late 1980s, people were finally beginning to rediscover natural farming as an alternative to the Chemical Age. Sure enough, it turns out that there are natural products that can do what the chemicals did without damaging the soil and rivers. Someday farmers and citizens will look back at our former agricultural practices and wonder "how could people do that?" And someday people will look back on the Chemical Age of Athletics and wonder why it all took place.

Consider yourself a pioneer in the new world of natural athletics. It may not instantly make you the most popular kid on the block (chemical abusers may feel threatened) but give them no mind. In the long run, like the tortoise and the hare, you will be the winner. And with your balanced outlook and perspectives you will have an active, healthy body that you can enjoy all of your long life. Best of luck in your pursuit. It might take a bit longer, but in the end it will be worth it. So get on with your training, focus your mental and physical energies on the task at hand, and go for it! Achieve your sport goals and create that body you have always wanted!

CHAPTER TWO

Strongmen And Muscle Beach

Throughout history, men and women have looked up to strong athletic individuals. This image of physical strength and athletic ability has been admired in every culture and during every time period. It is one of the constants of the human race.

Sports and body building activities have been an integral part of society for centuries. They continue to be. What has changed in the last three decades—a mere blink of the eye in terms of our civilization—is that steroids have invaded sports. What used to be a healthy striving for excellence in sports has become for many a competition between pharmaceuticals, a battle where the quantity of chemicals you take determines how well you score. This perversion of the ideal of sports can sometimes seem so all-encompassing, however, that it is helpful to look back in time and see just how recent and transitory this steroid invasion has been.

The Early Years

Back when we all lived in caves we were very physical as a people—we had to be. We lifted stones and logs to furnish our homes and make fires. We migrated over vast distances to hunt and forage for food. These activities kept us fairly fit from a cardiovascular point of view—provided there was enough food. Obviously, the activities of daily existence occupied most of our waking hours. Sports were not a high priority.

As society evolved, however, there was more free time and a greater division of responsibilities. Hierarchies were created with leaders and classes. As a rule, the leaders in those days were strong men who ruled by their physical dominance. The people in these societies looked up to those who had strength above the ordinary—a trait that a majority of men strived for. These heroes of old were usually powerful warriors or physically active individuals.

These first societies evolved into the civilizations of Greece and Rome. In Greece, of course, the first Olympics were held. There was also an appreciation for the physique as a thing of beauty. Socrates is said to have felt that:

> No man has a right to be an amateur in the matter of physical training. It is a shame for a man to grow old without seeing the beauty and strength of which his body is capable.

Milo, a Greek born in 558 BC, was the first known weight lifter. He carried a bull on his shoulders the entire length of the stadium at Olympia, a feat which he accomplished using an early form of progressive-resistance training—picking up the bull every day from its birth so that his strength grew as the animal's weight increased. The Greeks were known for their athletic gods, including Atlas and Hercules. They also first developed the ideal of being a whole man: striving for the best in all aspects of a person's physical and mental development.

During the Middle Ages sports were limited to jousts between knights, who competed for the amusement of royalty. There were strongman legends, of course, like the English Beowulf and King Arthur, but fitness was seen as a requirement of survival. Later, the Renaissance brought an appreciation for the beauty of the body, as seen in the many works of Michelangelo. The vast majority of the population, however, were peasants with other things on their minds.

Before the Industrial Revolution the hard life on the farms kept most people fit from a strength point of view, and there was little time for sports. Once people began moving to the cities, however, and started working at offices and factories, things began to change. The need for cardiovascular conditioning, plus an increased recognition of the role that recreation can play in a balanced life, led to a greater focus on fitness.

By the 1830s many upper- and middle-class people began to exercise to bring excitement to their sedentary lives. German immigrants, who arrived in America following the European revolutions of the late 1840s, started building gymnasiums called Turnveriens where they would do tumbling exercises and play ball. The Czechs set up the Sokol clubs. These gyms served as social centers that helped build community spirit. The only equipment, however, were medicine balls, hoops and Indian clubs.

Churches picked up on the fitness craze to boost their popularity. The Muscular Christianity movement, which started in England and spread to the United States, combined physical conditioning with a strong dose of moral medicine. Many of the large churches built during this period included gymnasiums along with their religious facilities. It was here that the idea of a mind-body connection was first popularized. The faithful were instructed that the discipline needed in gymnastics was also required for leading a moral life. The Young Men's Christian Association (YMCA) and the Young Men's Hebrew Association (YMHA) both added fitness facilities to their layouts during this period and championed the moral physical lifestyle. This orientation continues today.

By the end of the 1800s physical fitness took on new dimensions. The modern Olympic Movement began with the first Olympics in 1896. This led to a heightened sense of nationalistic pride as teams from various countries competed for the Gold. More Americans became involved in outdoor activities. This movement was encouraged by "roughrider" President Teddy Roosevelt, who personified the fitness craze with his wilderness expeditions.

During this period strongmen began to gain popularity at the carnivals and traveling shows of the day. These men impressed their audiences with feats of strength such as lifting anvils, cannons or even platforms with people on them. One of the most famous was Eugene Sandow, who made his reputation in Europe and then came to the United States as "The World's Strongest Man." Sandow was unique in that he was very strong and aesthetically attractive at the same time. He had perfect body symmetry and is now considered the father of bodybuilding. His popularity caused sales of exercise equipment to skyrocket, as people rediscovered the aesthetic qualities of the physique.

Around the same time, the first fitness "personalities" became popular. Dioclesian Lewis published books and wrote numerous articles on physical fitness, and opened the first specialized fitness facility. He also encouraged women and children to get involved in the fitness craze, which had previously been limited to men. George Hackenschmidt, a world class wrestler and weightlifter, also published books on fitness and life.

The first bodybuilding contests were held during this period. Bernarr Macfadden, who was publisher of ***Physical Culture*** (the first bodybuilding magazine ever), organized the Most Perfectly Developed Man in America competition in 1903 at Madison Square Garden in New York. At Macfadden's contest in 1921, the winner was a young man named Angelo Siciliano. Angelo later changed his name to Charles Atlas and became a legend with his advertisements for "dynamic tension" in comic books and magazines. These ads continued for almost 50 years.

In the early 1930s the next great fitness personality became popular: Jack LaLanne. Starting with a gym in Oakland in 1936, Jack LaLanne eventually became a household name with his highly popular television shows. And by making exercise an acceptable part of mainstream America, he changed the perception of physical fitness for generations to come.

The first Mr. America contest was held in 1939 in New York. The winner, Bert Goodrich, was an all-around athlete and Hollywood stuntman, who dazzled the judges with a tumbling exhibition. The next year, John Grimek won the show. He then came back the following year and won it again, convincing the Amateur Athletic Union (AAU) to make a rule that you could only win the Mr. America once. Another legendary bodybuilder from this period was Sigmund Klein, who once called bodybuilding "a very serious performance of art."

Bob Hoffman was another famous weightlifter and athlete from the period. He bought the York Barbell Company in the early 1930s and turned it into an internationally famous institution. He also published a book in 1940 called ***Secrets of Strength and Development***, which became a best seller. In it, Hoffman notes:

> Breathes there a man with soul so dead,
> who never to himself hath said,
> I want to be strong and well developed.

Meanwhile, on the West Coast, a phenomenon known as Muscle Beach was taking hold. From 1934 on, athletes would come to Santa Monica Beach to perform on the sand for the crowds. At first they used some old carpet for a mat. Soon, Muscle Beach grew into a major attraction with a permanent platform, gymnastic equipment and rings. Every weekend crowds from all over the world would come to watch the incredible acrobatics and feats of strength. The first bodybuilding contests in California were held here too, as well as weightlifting exhibitions and beauty contests.

Athletes like Vic Tanny, Jack LaLanne, Bert Goodrich, Steve Reeves and George Eiferman were regulars at Muscle Beach, as was Harold Zinkin, the inventor of the Universal exercise machine. All of these men went on to become pillars of their sports, setting the stage for the fitness revolution to come. Muscle Beach remained popular with the public for over twenty years in Santa Monica, and continues today in nearby Venice, California.

The athletes from this period say there was a camaraderie then that doesn't always exist today. There was a sense of fraternity, when people just got together and trained for the pure enjoyment of it. Winning a trophy wasn't everything. The goal of these athletes was physical culture—the building of their bodies into a physical perfection that would last their entire lives.

The word steroid hasn't been used so far in this entire history of sports and fitness. With good reason. These drugs hadn't been invented yet. All of the achievements of the Strongmen and the athletes of Muscle Beach took place without a single steroid entering their systems. These athletes respected their bodies and took it for granted that everyone else would too. After all, health is the primary purpose of athletics, right? Little did these people know what awaited sports competition in the next few decades.

Since World War II

Steroids were first discovered during World War II as a result of German experiments aimed at creating a race of Aryan supermen. After the War, it was realized that these drugs could aid in the recovery of famine and war victims, since steroids enhance the body's recuperative system and accelerate the regrowth of muscle tissue. These remain the primary medical uses of steroids to this day.

After World War II, of course, the Cold War began. This battle for political influence and control impacted many areas of our lives, including sports. Olympic competitions became arenas for ideological battle, as both sides found symbolic value in the victories of their athletes. The increased importance of these competitions lead some athletes and coaches to adopt a win-at-all-costs mentality that seemed to justify steroid abuse. There were continual rumors about how the socialist countries condoned or even required mega-dosages of drugs for their athletes. This seemed to free Western athletes from blame, since they were just "leveling the playing field," as it were. The fact that these drugs harmed the athletes that used them somehow got lost in this Olympic battle for ideas.

Despite these political frictions, the period since World War II has been a time of progress in many areas. There has been a much greater emphasis on fitness in the general population. Technological break-throughs and labor-saving devices have created more free time, and many people are taking advantage of this time to get in shape. There has been a lot more involvement in sports activities by the public, and the number of persons exercising regularly has skyrocketed. It has been a bumpy road, however.

In 1956 President Dwight Eisenhower set up the President's Council on Youth Fitness. Schools set up fitness tests for students which measured strength and speed, including calisthenics and running. This program produced solid gains in student performance for over a decade, but then disappeared from schools by the late 1960s.

In 1962 another craze took hold in America: the RCAF, or Royal Canadian Air Force exercise programs. These programs required no equipment and could be done at home in under 15 minutes. The men's program (5BX) had five exercises, while the women's (XBX) had ten. RCAF was all the rage during the 1960s, building on the President's fitness program. Yet it soon began to lose its appeal as the public moved on to other things.

Bodybuilding began to capture the public eye during the 1960s. Every year more contests were being held throughout the country as the Iron Game attracted greater numbers of athletes. As a spectator sport it grew by leaps and bounds. Yet the numbers of competitors on steroids also continued to grow as these drugs became more and more available.

In 1968 Dr. Kenneth Cooper published his book **Aerobics**, which helped begin a fitness phenomenon that continues today. Although the idea of cardiovascular conditioning had been around for a while, Cooper's book was well documented and appeared at a time when heart disease was on the rise. While we now know that diet plays an important role along with exercise in reducing heart problems, the recognition that anything could be done to prevent what had been considered "fate" lead to a revolution in public thinking.

This revolution was soon picked up on by a variety of authors and enthusiasts. ***The Complete Book of Running***, by Jim Fixx (1977), gave a boost to the idea of aerobic conditioning by showing a personal success story (Jim had been rather fat and a chain smoker yet went on to run marathons). His book also talked about the mental and physical benefits of running, and brought marathoning into the mainstream. It gave a generation of people the push they needed to get out there and start jogging.

Soon, almost everyone was in on the act. Jane Fonda made millions with her exercise videos. Richard Simmons preached to the couch potato set and inspired them to spend more time working out and less watching soap operas. Stores sold shelves full of tapes and books to the eager public, while the level of sports involvement soared. The result: a society that as a whole is more health conscious than any other in history.

Everyone benefits from these sport activities. Recreational sports provide a release from the tensions of the day, giving us time to unwind, relax and refresh ourselves. We can also take out our aggressions in a socially acceptable manner (beats socking it to the boss—even if he or she deserves it!) Sports are competitive activities that help foster ideas about striving for a goal and outperforming someone else, of struggling and winning. They channel our feelings toward each other in a positive way that encourages friendship and "sportsmanship", integrity and fair play. They help us relate to each other, bonding us in a way nothing else can. What can compare to Superbowl Sunday or the World Series? These are annual events that mark the passage of time in our lives—moments we use as guideposts.

There is also a growing understanding that people need to tap into the physical *and* mental parts of themselves in order to have a complete and fulfilling life. This is not some weird fringe element idea anymore. Many world leaders jog nowadays. Corporations are joining the fitness movement and providing gyms for their employees. Some even give employees the equivalent of time off by including exercise as part of the corporate regimen. Studies have shown that these exercise programs increase productivity and reduce sick leave, while decreasing the tensions and frustrations that come along with high-level pressure cooker executive jobs. This increased satisfaction leads to greater motivation and higher work intensity. So we all gain from increased physical activity, both as individuals and as a nation.

The fitness revolution has made major gains. Everyone has a higher consciousness about physical fitness than even a generation ago. Many plan their schedules so there is time for a jog or a trip to the gym, and feel bad when they miss it. As a society we have accepted the challenge of trying to "build strong bodies 12 ways" (although eating white bread isn't the way to do it), and we look forward to long, physically rewarding lives.

There is also an increasing importance placed on nutrition. Not so long ago people who cared about their fat and cholesterol intake were considered a bit weird. Now everyone accepts the fact that diet and nutrition have a major impact on their health and well-being. People are cleaning up their acts, as it were, and choosing healthier foods. The food industry, including the fast-food restaurants, are responding to these demands by providing more wholesome products. Sales of nutrition books have skyrocketed, and names like Pritikin have become household words. It's all part of a very encouraging trend that will bring major benefits to society as a whole, reducing the cost of health care and improving our collective quality of life.

Bodybuilding has shared in this fitness phenomenon. It is now an accepted mainstream sport, with televised coverage of major events and an active professional contest circuit. Each year more and more athletes from other sports, like football and wrestling, are crossing over to compete on the posing dais. As its popularity grows, it takes its rightful place among the major sports of our day, and may soon make it into the Olympics. The major obstacle holding bodybuilding back is the widespread use of steroids. Once this problem is solved (and it will be), bodybuilding will gain even greater respect from the public as the healthy lifelong sport activity it always should have been.

The future looks bright for sports of all types. After steroid use has been eliminated, sports will regain their proper place in society. Professional sports will always be intensely competitive, as they should be, but the competition will once again be based on real person-to-person differences, and not on the variations caused by substance abuse. This will bring sports back to the Olympian ideal of fair play and the promotion of sound bodies.

It's time to make the commitment to lead a healthy and athletic life. You can carry on the tradition of the Strongmen and Muscle Beach athletes by casting drugs aside and training for your long-term health, just as they did. Your personal commitment to be a natural athlete will be repeated a million times over as our society says no to drugs. This will bring us back to the days when sports competitions are unblemished by pharmaceutical battles, when the ethic of honest sportsmanship will once again reign supreme!

There's no question about it. You *can* excel in sports without steroids once you know the right way to go about it. So have you made your commitment? Great! Now let's get on with it!

FOREVER NATURAL

CHAPTER THREE

Muscular Development

Our bodies are intricate, complex entities—one of the true marvels of Nature. Our abilities to think, survive and grow result from an incredible number of chemical actions and reactions so detailed that they inspire a sense of awe. Once these interactions are understood, an appreciation for its natural functioning develops that makes the thought of putting steroids into the body seem like pure folly. In this chapter the nature of these interactions is discussed, with a focus on the process of muscular growth and development. This will provide you with valuable information that you can use to improve your athletic training.

The muscles allow the body to stand upright and move in a coordinated fashion. Each muscle connects two bones, and the entire network of skeletal muscles and bones is called the bony lever system. Muscles are connected to the outer coating of the bones by tendons—strong and densely constructed connective tissues that allow the force of muscular contraction to be transmitted from the muscle cells to the outer reaches of the bones.

The point at which the muscle/tendon connects to the relatively stable part of the skeleton is called the muscle's origin. The point where the muscle/tendon attaches to the bone that performs the movement is known as the insertion. The locations of these origins and insertions are permanent, and cannot be modified through training. Therefore, if a person has a genetically short bicep, that muscle trait will always remain. The bicep can increase in size through muscle growth, but it cannot grow outward by changing its connection points to the bones. This is one of the "givens" that we all have to live with.

Muscle Contraction and Growth

There are more than 430 muscles in the body which permit voluntary motion. While each of these muscles has a specific function, all muscles share many characteristics in common. Skeletal muscle is made up principally of water, which accounts for over 75 percent of its weight. Another 20 percent of the muscle is protein, while the other 5 percent is made up of a variety of inorganic salts and other substances, including high-energy phosphates (an immediate energy source), minerals, enzymes, amino acids, fatty acids and the carbohydrate glucose.

Each muscle is covered with a wrapping of fibrous connective tissue that gives it form and helps protect it from injury. There are also several other fibrous tissues within the muscle itself that help in these functions. The basic unit of the muscle is the muscle fiber, which runs lengthwise within the muscle. There are approximately 250 million muscle fibers in the human body. It is the action of these muscle fibers that allows the muscles to contract.

The muscle fiber is not a single mass. When viewed at the microscopic level it is actually a complex assembly of numerous elements. The fiber is made up of many smaller parts called myofibrils, each no larger than a micron (0.00004 inch). These myofibrils run lengthwise through the muscle. Each of the myofibrils, in turn, is comprised of even smaller subunits called sarcomeres, which are the functional units of the muscle fiber. It is within the sarcomere that the contractile action of muscle takes place.

There are two types of protein-based myofilaments within the sarcomere—a thin actin filament and a thicker myosin filament. The actin is attached to the outer edge of the sarcomere, while the myosin is in its center. When viewed from the side, these two filaments appear to be on top of each other, like a layer cake.

The larger myosin filaments have small projections on them called crossbridges. These crossbridges extend from the body of the myosin and, when chemically "excited" in the presence of calcium, connect to the actin filaments at specific receptor sites. The crossbridges then

20

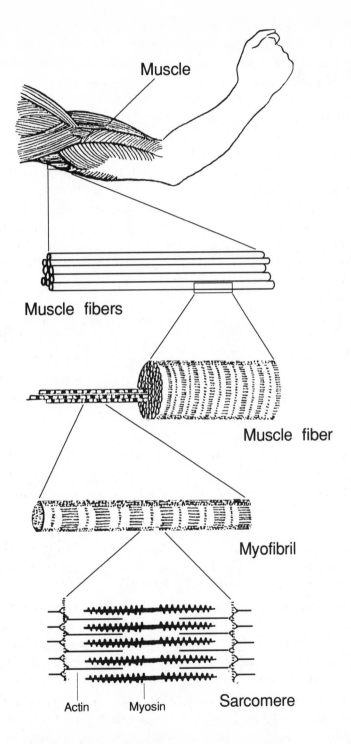

Muscle

Muscle fibers

Muscle fiber

Myofibril

Actin   Myosin   Sarcomere

Figure 1 - Muscle Components

grab onto the actin much like the hands of a person climbing a rope, forcing the actin filament towards the center of the sarcomere while the myosin filament moves toward its outer edge. As a result, the two filaments "slide" past each other, causing a reduction in the length of the sarcomere. This microscopic contraction, when multiplied by the millions of sarcomeres in the muscle fiber (and the thousands of fibers in the entire muscle) is what causes muscle contraction. All muscular movement is caused by this sliding of filaments within the sarcomere.

There is still debate among scientists as to how muscles grow. Some laboratory experiments have shown that new muscle fibers can form under certain circumstances, at least in animals. It is usually agreed, however, that most, if not all, of the growth in human skeletal muscle is caused by an increase in the number of sarcomeres within the muscle fiber and by an increase in the number and thickness of the myofilaments, which enlarges the size of each sarcomere.

These changes are the result of improved protein synthesis within the muscle cell. This muscle growth, called hypertrophy, improves the muscle's ability to generate tension. It also increases the amount of glycogen—the storage form of glucose—that is stored in the muscle fiber. (This glucose is frequently called blood sugar.) It is important to note that hypertrophy only occurs in response to an increased demand placed on the muscle by the body, that is, by making the muscle work harder than it ever has before.

Natural athletes who seek greater muscle mass need to keep this in mind, since a muscle can increase in size only when stimulated by a greater overload than it has experienced before. This increased overload can be achieved in three ways—by increasing the duration (length), frequency or intensity of the exercises you do. These points are discussed in greater detail in the chapters **The Eight Training Principles** and **A Natural Exercise Program**.

The Three Energy Sources

All of the mechanical energy produced by the body is generated through a series of chemical reactions within the body's tissues. The raw materials for these reactions are the foods we eat—the carbohydrates, fats and proteins in our diet. These foods are by and large digested in the stomach and assimilated in the intestines. Many go through additional chemical changes in the liver. The broken-down food components are then converted by a series of reactions into a chemical called ATP (adenosine triphosphate). These reactions conserve a great deal of the energy in food as ATP. The remainder is lost as body heat.

ATP is known as the body's "energy currency." It is used for building new tissue, nerve transmission, digestion, gland secretions and, of course, for muscle contraction. As its name implies, ATP has three phosphate molecules bonded to an adenosine molecule. When one of the bonds connecting the phosphate molecules is broken, a great deal of energy is created. It is this breaking of bonds between molecules that produces all of the energy utilized by the body.

There are three main pathways for the energy production the body needs to live and grow. This energy is produced by complex reactions that occur within the cell, and all involve the use of ATP in differing ways as the basis for energy production. Two of these three energy pathways are called anaerobic energy systems, which means that the chemical processes producing the energy do not utilize oxygen. These sources are the ATP-CP system and glycolysis. The third pathway utilizes oxygen in its chemical reactions and is referred to as the aerobic system.

The first system, ATP-CP, is used as the immediate source of energy for the body. Activities such as the 100-yard dash and powerlifting, which require rapid and immediate energy for maximal exercise, are heavily dependent on the ATP-CP system, especially at the beginning. This system involves an exchange of energy between two molecules, ATP and CP (creatine phosphate). This reversible process goes on constantly at the start of physical work, since there is only about three ounces of ATP in the body at any one time—enough to provide maximal energy for only a couple of seconds. The main advantage of this energy system is that it can go to work immediately, something that the other energy systems cannot do. If it weren't for the ATP-CP system, we would be unable to sprint, lift heavy weights or do any other work that requires immediate full effort. We would have to start track and field events in slow motion. ATP-CP therefore fills the gap between the start of exercise and the time when the other two systems kick in.

The second anaerobic system is glycolysis. This system provides most of the energy for medium-duration activities like weightlifting, wrestling and sprint swimming. During glycolysis a glucose molecule enters the cell from the blood and is transformed into an end product called pyruvic acid through a series of complex reactions. These reactions allow a significant amount of energy to be produced quickly for muscular contraction just as the ATP-CP system begins to run out of steam. Glycolysis can also use muscle glycogen (the storage form of glucose) and the glycerol formed when a fat molecule is broken down as its raw material for energy production.

Lactic acid and the amino acid alanine are byproducts of glycolysis. In the absence of adequate oxygen (anaerobic conditions) the pyruvic acid is converted into lactic acid and alanine, which actually helps keep glycolysis going by removing excess hydrogen ions that would normally grind it to a halt. The lactic acid escapes into the bloodstream and away from the muscle. This escape mechanism is only temporary, however, because the level of lactic acid in the blood and muscle eventually increases. This increased acidity inactivates some of the enzymes used in glycolysis, which reduces the ability of the muscles to contract. Fatigue sets in and exercise must stop.

Lactic acid is usually considered to be a waste product—an unfortunate part of working out that we all must live with. This is not the case. Lactic acid is actually a valuable source of chemical energy that is stored by the body during exercise until sufficient oxygen is available. In the presence of adequate oxygen, lactic acid is converted back into pyruvic acid, ready for use as an energy source. Without lactic acid, glycolysis would run into a dead end and fatigue would set in even earlier. Alanine, lactic acid and pyruvic acid can also be converted back into glucose in the liver, providing more raw material for future energy. So lactic acid formation is simply part of the body's complex biological system. Everything has its purpose.

The third type of energy production is the aerobic system. This system releases 95 percent of the potential energy in each glucose or fat molecule through a complex set of processes called the Krebs cycle, which can only function in the presence of oxygen. This aerobic system makes use of the mitochondria in each cell, which are also known as the cell's "energy factories."

It is important to remember that many sports use anaerobic energy systems to provide much of their energy requirements. Bodybuilding, powerlifting and sprinting use anaerobic systems for virtually all of their energy production. As a result, you can't burn a lot of fat while lifting weights. That can only be done by participating in aerobic activities, such as walking, bicycling, jogging, etc.

All three energy systems are interrelated. Rather than switching on and off like the lights of a traffic signal, the three systems overlap to provide a smooth blending from one means of energy production to another. This allows the body to perform at its best through all levels of exercise intensity. It also appears that the energy systems can adapt to training, becoming more efficient in their operations. As a result, natural athletes should train using the same energy system that they will use during their competitions.

Most of the potential energy in the body is stored in the form of fat (adipose tissue). In fact, the body's reserve of carbohydrate energy is limited to about 2,000 calories. Three-quarters of this is muscle glycogen, and most of the rest is stored as glycogen in the liver. Any carbohydrate intake beyond these storage limits is eventually converted to body fat for storage. When it is needed, these fat molecules are then broken down to produce energy. Fat molecules are a prolific source of energy, creating over 12 times the amount of ATP produced by a molecule of glucose.

Muscle Fiber Types

There are two major types of muscle fibers: fast-twitch (FT) and slow-twitch (ST). Everybody has both types of fibers in their muscles, but the relative amount that a person has of each can vary widely. Some athletes, in fact, have fast- to slow-fiber ratios as high as 8 or 9 to 1, while most persons have more equal proportions of each. This fiber ratio, which can even vary between the muscles of the same person, is determined by genetics and cannot be altered significantly by training. All muscle fibers, however, respond to athletic training by improving their abilities to perform.

Fast-twitch fibers, as their name implies, contract rapidly in response to a stimulus. They also have a high capacity for producing ATP during glycolysis due to their ability to release calcium quickly during exercise (which aids in speedy muscle contraction). The FT fibers are used almost exclusively for activities which demand a rapid production of power, such as weightlifting and sprinting, and in those situations where stop-and-go movements are required, as in basketball and volleyball. In fact, FT fibers can contract and develop tension twice as quickly as the slow-twitch fibers. The fast-twitch fibers also increase the most in size. This is due to the relatively greater enlargement of their actin and myosin filaments and the increase in total glycogen content in these muscle fibers.

Slow-twitch fibers, on the other hand, are called into use when a slow speed of contraction is required. These fibers are well-suited to less intensive aerobic activities because of their superior ability to produce ATP aerobically. This ability is due to the greater blood flow in this type of fiber and to the larger number of mitochondria in the cells, which contain a large amount of myoglobin—a reddish-colored compound that helps to store and transport oxygen to the muscle cell. It is for this reason that ST fibers are sometimes called red fibers.

Slow-twitch fibers are relatively resistant to fatigue and are therefore well-suited to prolonged aerobic exercise. This is due to the larger amounts of certain enzymes found in these fibers, which help them utilize fatty acids in the body. ST fibers can therefore sustain endurance-type activities, which require the use of the body's system of aerobic energy production. ST fibers can also produce energy anaerobically if need be, but they are not as efficient at it as the FT fibers.

While there has been some evidence of muscle fibers changing from FT to ST due to intense endurance training, by and large the relative proportion of fibers each of us has remains constant throughout our lives. This can be an advantage or a disadvantage, depending on the particular sport you wish to excel in. As a result, a natural athlete's muscle fiber composition can actually impact the degree of success he or she has in a particular sport. It should be noted, however, that many sports require both types of muscle fibers to differing degrees.

Nerves and Muscle Movement

While fiber composition is an important consideration in muscle movement, it is not the only factor. The central nervous system plays a vital role in controlling these movements—sending the impulses that cause the muscles to contract and stopping these contractions when sensors indicate that muscle damage may occur. This coordinated system of neural circuits in the brain and spinal cord functions like a computer. In response to changes in internal and external stimuli, sensory input is received, organized and then transmitted back to the muscles, where the desired actions take place. Without the nervous system, the muscles would be unable to move.

The nervous system consists of the brain, spinal cord and nerve fibers. In the back of the brain is the cerebellum, which is the center for muscular control. This specialized brain tissue is responsible for posture and maintaining the tone of the muscles at rest. The cerebellum is also involved in equilibrium, movement, perception of speed and several reflex functions. It is here that all the "fine tuning" of muscular activity takes place.

The spinal cord serves as the connection between the brain and the motoneurons which actually interact with the muscles. There are two types of motoneurons, or nerve fibers, that are essential for muscle movement: afferent and efferent. Since the electrical stimuli travel through these fibers in a particular direction, they are known as nerve pathways. The afferent pathways transmit sensory impulses from the muscles to the spinal cord. These impulses tell the brain and spinal cord how much tension is being produced by the muscle.

The efferent pathways transmit the signals from the brain and spinal cord back to the muscle, ordering it to perform in a certain way. The degree of tension produced is therefore dependent on the signal the muscle receives from the brain. Strength is mentally determined. This is important to remember, because steroids do not appear to affect the functioning of the nervous system at all. If you can train your brain to maximize the nerve impulses it sends to the muscle, you will be able to lift as much as someone else your size who is on drugs. It's that simple.

Some of the actions of the nervous system actually occur within the spinal cord. There are 31 spinal cord segments, each of which connects to a group of afferent and efferent nerve fibers. Simple reflex actions, like pulling away from a hot object, take place in these segments. You may have noticed that your finger pulls away from an object before you actually "feel" the heat. This is because the reflex action takes place in the spinal cord, while the actual heat sensation occurs in the brain. The extra time it takes to reach the brain is responsible for the delay in "feeling" the pain.

There are about 420,000 motoneurons in the human body. Since the body has nearly 250 million muscle fibers, it is clear that each nerve connects to many different muscle fibers. The exact number of muscle fibers per nerve depends on the function of the muscle. Where the muscle is called upon to perform detailed and precise work, like in the eye, a neuron may control fewer than ten muscle fibers. Bigger muscles like the legs, where the movements are less complex, can have up to 2,000 muscle fibers per nerve.

This network of nerve and muscle fibers is called a motor unit. The muscle fibers in a particular motor unit are all of the same type, that is, either fast-twitch or slow-twitch. All of the fibers will therefore have the same metabolic and contractile properties. Fast-twitch motor units are innervated by large motoneurons that are able to transmit electrical messages quickly. They also reach a higher level of peak tension and can reach that level almost twice as fast as the slow-twitch motor units. Slow-twitch units, on the other hand, are innervated by small motoneurons that conduct messages much more slowly. They are more resistant to fatigue, however. All muscles contain both types of motor units.

If an electrical stimulus is strong enough to reach the action threshold of the motoneuron, all of the muscle fibers in that motor unit will contract simultaneously. There is no such thing as a strong or weak contraction from a motor unit—either all of the muscle fibers contract or none of them does. This is called the all-or-none principle. Variations in the intensity of muscle contraction occur by changing the number of motor units recruited for a particular activity and by changing the frequency at which the motoneuron "fires" its electrical stimulus. (If a second stimulus reaches the muscle before it has relaxed from the last stimulus, the total amount of tension is increased.) By these two mechanisms, the brain and muscles are capable of achieving a full range of contractions, producing just the right amount of force necessary to achieve the desired movement.

This ability to recruit motor units can actually be modified through training. Therefore, by focusing your efforts over time, you can train your mind to "fire" more of the needed motor units at the right time, maximizing the total force produced. This will allow the power athlete to lift heavier weights and stimulate the greatest amount of hypertrophy in his or her muscles.

The brain selectively recruits the fast- or slow-twitch motor units, depending on the particular activity needed. During sustained endurance activities like jogging, the slow-twitch units are recruited, while during quick, powerful movements like weightlifting the fast-twitch units are called into action as well. As a result, a limited amount of endurance exercise ("aerobics") will not hurt your progress in weight training, since fast-twitch motor-unit recruitment is limited in aerobic activities.

In order to make sure that high-intensity exercise does not damage the muscle, there are a number of sensory receptors in the muscle that are sensitive to tension, pressure and stretch. These receptors continually send information over the afferent pathways to the central nervous system for processing, which provides an ongoing feedback mechanism for the muscles. The two main types of receptors are the muscle spindles and the Golgi tendon organs.

The muscle spindles provide the brain with information on the length and tension of the muscle. If there is an excessive stretch on the muscle, the spindles set up a stretch reflex action that results in a stronger contraction. This stretch reflex can be used to increase the total force of contraction on your resistance exercises. The spindles, which contain the muscle proteins actin and myosin, wrap around the muscle fibers and are capable of contracting. There are more spindles in muscles requiring complex movements than in muscles with more simple functions.

The Golgi tendon organs also protect the muscle from injury. These receptors are located on the tendons which connect the muscles to the bones. If the muscle tries to exert a force that is too great for it to handle, the Golgi organ sends a signal that reduces the activity of the motoneuron. This decreases the tension level generated in the muscle and keeps it from being damaged. As the muscle grows stronger, the Golgi organ is able to sense this increased strength and adapts accordingly. It is an adjustable safety valve that looks out for the long-term best interests of your muscle.

Muscle Soreness and Recuperation

Every natural athlete who has pushed him- or herself to the max knows the feeling of muscle soreness. The concept of "no pain, no gain" can even make this soreness a desirable thing—something to be sought after. Many people like this pain sensation, figuring that the soreness means they must be getting results from all the time and effort they put into their training. Unfortunately, there is no evidence that muscle soreness helps muscle growth.

There are actually two types of soreness. The first type is the burn—the immediate sensation that occurs while the exercise is being performed. This burn begins slowly and builds to a level so intense and painful that exercise must stop. This is due to the buildup of lactic acid in the muscle, which is a byproduct of the anaerobic system (glycolysis) used to produce the energy to do the exercise. (As was mentioned earlier, lactic acid buildup is actually a positive thing, since it helps the body conserve energy that would otherwise be wasted.)

This type of soreness goes away fairly quickly, allowing the athlete to perform another exercise seconds after completing the last set. In fact, almost 90 percent of this lactic acid is converted into other products by the body within 50 minutes. Therefore, lactic acid buildup is not the cause of the delayed onset muscle soreness that can occur 24 to 48 hours after exercise.

Delayed onset muscle soreness can vary from a mild sensation to a pain so intense that muscle function is affected. Intense muscle soreness is almost always felt by natural athletes when they begin weight training. After their bodies have adjusted to progressive-resistance training, however, the degree of soreness experienced depends on the individual. A day or two after a session of heavy squats, some athletes can barely climb stairs or get up from a chair, while other equally developed lifters doing the exact same weight experience only mild pain. Soreness can occur after even moderate exercise, especially if the athlete has not trained in a while. It can also begin anywhere from eight to 12 hours after exercise, reach a peak in intensity one to two days later and persist for two to seven days. There is still no explanation for these wide individual differences in muscle soreness.

However, there are several theories to explain why soreness occurs. The two that are most accepted nowadays are the tear theory and the theory of connective tissue damage. The tear theory proposes that minute tears or ruptures of individual fibers (and the sarcomeres within fibers) are the cause of the soreness. This theory correlates well with the observation that eccentric, or lengthening, exercises (frequently called negatives) cause more muscle soreness than concentric (shortening) or isometric (static) contractions.

It is felt that eccentric movements produce greater soreness because, compared to concentric movements, fewer fibers are recruited for a particular muscular effort. That is, when an athlete exercises with a barbell, fewer muscle fibers are called into action to lower the bar than to lift it in the first place. This increases the tension produced per fiber, resulting in greater tearing and damage to each individual fiber. A marked increase in the levels of certain muscle enzymes has been noted in the blood, particularly after eccentric exercise. This escape of enzymes from the muscle cells suggests that some damage to the fibers has indeed taken place.

The second theory holds that muscle soreness is caused by damage to the connective tissue in and around the muscles, as well as by an exercise-induced imbalance in the metabolism of collagen (a major component of the connective tissue). It is also possible that the soreness results from damage to the muscle fibers *and* the connective tissues, so that both theories are correct.

Slow static stretching after exercise has been shown to help reduce immediate muscle soreness (the "burn"). When doing a static stretch, it is essential to relax the muscle without bouncing as you try to extend it to its greatest length. A bouncing stretch, on the other hand, can actually prolong soreness by stimulating the muscle to contract in a reflex action, causing additional muscle damage and possible muscle spasms.

There are several factors which influence the time it takes to recuperate from exercise and related muscle soreness. As a rule, the larger muscle groups and bigger muscles take longer to recover than do smaller muscles and muscle groups. Exercises performed with heavy weights for a few repetitions seem to cause more soreness than when a greater number of repetitions are done using a lighter weight. Age is also a factor, with older athletes needing more time to recuperate. Proper nutrition can shorten recovery time, while alcohol and most other recreational drugs lengthen it. And, of course, a healthy body without disease can recuperate faster than an unhealthy one. These concepts are discussed at greater length later in this book.

Hormones and the Endocrine System

The body's endocrine system plays a major role in promoting muscle development. This complex system serves as a major link in the body's internal communications, helping to maintain stability (homeostasis) by manipulating the levels of various chemical substances. The endocrine system consists of a number of host organs (glands), minute quantities of chemical messengers (hormones) and several receptor or target organs. There are some 23 hormones in the human body, many of which are involved in multiple functions. Here the hormones relating to muscle development are discussed.

Hormones regulate almost all of the body's metabolic reactions. Most hormonal secretions are under the direct or indirect control of the hypothalamus, a portion of the brain located near the point where the spinal cord connects to the brain. As a result, the nervous system and the endocrine system act together to cause the desired effect in the body. While nerves produce quick but short-lived reactions, the glands provide slower, pulsating releases of hormones that complement the actions of the nerves. Together, these two systems are responsible for all body functions, including muscle growth.

The major function of hormones is to change the rate at which cellular actions take place. They do this by either altering the pace at which proteins are synthesized, by changing the timing of enzyme activities or by modifying the ability of certain materials to penetrate the membrane of the cell. In all cases the hormones interact with the cell at special receptor sites located either on the cell membrane or inside the cell. Man-made hormones, such as anabolic steroids and genetically engineered growth hormone, enter the cell in the exact same way.

PITUITARY GLAND

The pituitary gland, located next to the hypothalamus at the base of the brain, is the center of the endocrine system. At least eight different hormones are produced by the pituitary, including growth hormone (hGH), follicle-stimulating hormone (FSH) and luteinizing hormone (LH).

Growth hormone has a major role in muscle development due to its ability to promote cell division and proliferation throughout the body. It does this by increasing the amount of amino acids transported within the cell membrane, which provides the raw material for enhanced protein synthesis. It also increases nitrogen retention and stimulates the liver to produce various growth factors. HGH can increase the level of free fatty acids in the blood, resulting in greater use of fats as an energy source and the sparing of available carbohydrates. It also effects the growth of the bones and connective tissues (cartilage, tendons and ligaments).

Growth hormone is produced by the pituitary in response to a secretion of growth hormone releasing factor by the hypothalamus. This releasing factor, in turn, is produced when the hypothalamus is stimulated by exercise, as well as by stress and anxiety. Exercise results in high levels of hGH release, allowing the muscles to synthesize the proteins necessary for muscle hypertrophy. The greater the exercise intensity, the more growth hormone released.

It also seems that varying the overall intensity and the specific exercises in your natural training routine can keep the pituitary sensitive to the adaptive stresses of exercise, stimulating even greater hGH release. It should be noted, however, that overtraining and excessive amounts of eccentric movements (negatives) can actually reduce the level of growth hormone produced. A fine line exists between high intensity training and overtraining. You really can have too much of a good thing!

Several factors besides exercise have been shown to effect the amount of growth hormone released by the pituitary. The second greatest amount of hGH release occurs during the first 45 to 90 minutes of sleep, with smaller, pulsating peak releases at 90 minute intervals after that. The quality of sleep can affect these release rates, since frequent waking can disturb the body's hormonal patterns. Age can reduce the height and frequency of these releases, as can alcohol. Body fat affects growth hormone levels as well (the more fat, the less hGH produced).

It also appears that a high blood-glucose level can reduce hGH release to a limited extent. You should therefore try to eat your pre-workout meal a full hour before training. Also, finish your last meal of the day early enough so that your blood-glucose level can return to normal before going to sleep. On the other hand, crystalline arginine and ornithine supplements before bedtime do not appear to be effective in stimulating additional hGH release.

FSH and LH are two pituitary hormones that stimulate the male and female sex organs to secrete more of their own hormones. Follicle-stimulating hormone (FSH) promotes the growth of follicles in the ovaries and stimulates the ovaries to secrete estrogens, one of the female sex hormones. In men FSH encourages the growth of the testes and sperm production. Luteinizing hormone (LH) stimulates the testes to produce more of the male hormone testosterone. When the balance of these hormones is disrupted, negative consequences frequently develop. These are discussed in the next chapter.

The pituitary also produces the precursor molecule from which endorphins are made. Endorphins are special opium-like substances that act on the brain to cause the "exercise high"—that feeling of euphoria and exhilaration that all athletes are familiar with. Endorphins have been shown to increase the tolerance to pain, improve appetite control and reduce the levels of anger, tension and anxiety. They also stimulate the release of growth hormone and influence the production of several other hormones.

Exercise increases the level of endorphins in the blood to five times their level at rest, and endorphin concentrations in the brain are probably even higher. It also seems that the brain becomes more sensitive to endorphins over time, so that less is needed to achieve the same effect. Surely this is part of the reason why athletes get so "hooked" on their sports!

THYROID GLAND

The thyroid gland secretes thyroxine, which increases the metabolic rate of all cells. Thyroxine, in fact, can raise the body's basal metabolism by as much as four times. It also increases the rate of carbohydrate and fat metabolism, allowing a person to lose weight more rapidly. In most persons the thyroxine level is maintained relatively constant through an elaborate feedback system.

Some drug-abusing athletes take thyroxine supplements to diet for a competition, since it allows them to get greater muscle definition quickly without severe food restriction. There is also some evidence that these thyroxine supplements temporarily convert slow-twitch muscle fibers to fast-twitch fibers under certain circumstances. Unfortunately, the end result of this hormonal manipulation can be a shutdown in the body's natural thyroid production, even after the supplements are no longer taken. Conversely, some obese people claim that their fat condition is due to a thyroxine deficiency. While using this excuse may make them feel better, as a point of fact thyroid malfunctions are the cause of obesity in less than three percent of all cases.

ADRENAL GLANDS

The adrenal glands, which are located above the kidneys, secrete three main hormones related to muscle development: aldosterone, cortisol and the androgens. These hormones affect the body in different yet very significant ways. Aldosterone regulates the relative levels of sodium and potassium in the fluid spaces on both sides of the cell wall. These minerals, also called electrolytes, are important for nerve transmission and the functioning of the muscles. Aldosterone is also essential in controlling the total sodium concentration in the body.

Aldosterone plays a major role in fluid retention as well. When natural athletes use a sodium loading technique to temporarily reduce water retention outside of the cell wall, they are actually attempting to manipulate the body's aldosterone level. The drop in aldosterone secretion that accompanies sodium loading causes an increase in extracellular fluid. When all sodium is then eliminated from the diet, aldosterone secretion rises, temporarily forcing most of the extracellular fluid into the cell, increasing the muscle's size. High aldosterone levels are accompanied by increases in blood volumes and arterial blood pressure, however, so great care must be taken when sodium loading.

Another important adrenal hormone is cortisol. Cortisol stimulates the breakdown of dietary protein into its amino acid components, which makes it available for use in muscle growth. However, too much cortisol in the blood can lead to a muscle-wasting process called catabolism, which can cause a negative nitrogen balance in the body. Counterproductive levels of cortisol can be produced by stress and by excessive amounts of exercise.

Cortisol also increases the use of the fat stores for energy production. While this can help provide energy during prolonged aerobic exercise, too great a utilization of fat can result in a dangerous acidic condition known as ketosis. This frequently occurs when athletes resort to low-calorie, low-carbohydrate diets, which force the body to rely predominantly on its fat stores for energy.

The last type of hormone secreted by the adrenal glands is the androgens. Androgens are the hormones that cause male sex characteristics, such as increased facial hair and deepening of the voice. While the testes in the male produce by far the most androgens, some are secreted by the adrenal gland in both the male and the female. Excess androgen production in the female can result in certain masculinizing effects.

PANCREAS

The pancreas in another vital gland. The pancreas produces several digestive enzymes and is responsible for the production of insulin and glucagon—two hormones which together regulate the level of glucose metabolism in all body tissues except the brain. Insulin acts to decrease the level of blood glucose, also called blood sugar. It accomplishes this by increasing the rate at which glucose is transported through the cell membranes of muscle and adipose tissue. In the muscles this increases the amount of glucose available for immediate energy needs. If the glucose is not needed at that time, it is either stored as muscle glycogen or as body fat. Insulin also has an impact on the metabolism of fats and proteins.

The pancreas secretes glucagon to counteract the effects of insulin. The role of glucagon is to increase the level of blood glucose when it gets too low. It does this by stimulating the production of glucose in the liver, which releases it into the blood stream. This occurs frequently during exercise, when physical activity reduces the body's carbohydrate reserves dramatically. The most common type of diabetic has a pancreas that is unable to produce insulin as quickly as needed, producing dangerous swings in blood-sugar levels. An abnormally low blood-glucose level is referred to as hypoglycemia.

GONADS

Last, but by no means least, are the gonads, which produce estrogen and progesterone in the female ovaries and testosterone in the male testes. Estrogen and progesterone are responsible for promoting the female sex characteristics. Testosterone, on the other hand, is the hormone which produces the greater muscle mass associated with the male. Testosterone is crucial to muscular development, and it also plays a role in reducing body-fat levels. For this reason, chemists have gone to great lengths to produce artificial forms of testosterone (steroids) that supply athletes with a greater level of this hormone than exists in their systems naturally. In the following chapter the short-term benefits and long-term impacts of this steroid use are discussed.

The effects of natural testosterone are so great that they have been divided into the categories of anabolic and androgenic. Anabolic functions are those related to tissue development, while the androgenic functions are those related to male sex characteristics. Anabolic functions include increased skeletal muscle mass, reduced body fat, increased retention of nitrogen by the body and increased protein synthesis. The androgenic functions, on the other hand, are those associated with male puberty. Included in these functions are: increased density and changes in the pattern of body hair, deepening of the voice, increased oil production of the sebaceous glands (producing acne), increased sexual desire, growth in the male organs and increased aggressive behavior.

Studies have shown that moderate levels of exercise increase the level of testosterone in the blood. On the other hand, excessive exercise, especially endurance exercise like marathon racing, can actually reduce testosterone levels. Both effects are temporary, however, because natural testosterone production is tightly controlled by the secretions of FSH and LH from the pituitary. Due to these feedback systems, natural testosterone does not produce any of the negative side effects associated with steroids. The body's complex feedback system (when functioning well) assures that all hormone levels are maintained in healthy amounts. It is only when athletes tinker with the natural working of their bodies that the problems begin.

Genetics

Muscular development is influenced by many factors. Most of these factors are the same for all humans, such as the internal structure of the sarcomere. Others, like muscle fiber distribution, vary with the individual and are genetically determined. While all humans can improve their performance with training, and everyone should be encouraged to exercise for enjoyment and longevity, there are certain restraints which genetics places on athletic potential. These factors need to be highlighted so you can have a sound basis for understanding the full gamet of variables which influence your development as a natural athlete.

One of the main genetically determined factors, of course, is body structure. There are three main body types: ectomorphs, mesomorphs and endomorphs. This division of body structures is based on the relatively greater growth of particular layers of the embryo before birth, which results in a predominance of certain body characteristics. Ectomorphs are slender in appearance and have difficulty putting on muscle mass. Endomorphs, on the other hand, have thick bones, tend to be heavy and are frequently fat. They can easily put on body size but find it difficult to lose weight for competitions. The mesomorphs are in the middle, with moderate bone structures as well as balanced, muscular and often athletic physiques.

Many top bodybuilders are mesomorphs, while basketball players tend to be ectomorphs. Of course, there are natural athletes from each body type who excel in most every sport. It should also be emphasized that while only three theoretical body structures exist, in reality most everyone is a blend of all types, with variations in the levels of dominance. All three body structures respond to training and all should exercise for their personal satisfaction and health.

There also appears to be genetically set limit in the muscle mass that a drug-free individual can achieve. Once the person reaches this point there is no amount of training that will increase the hypertrophy of the muscle. This does not mean, however, that the natural athlete should stop working out. Continued training is necessary to maintain peak muscle mass. Exercise also provides many other physical and psychological benefits, all of which are independent of body size. Training (especially aerobic training) helps reduce body fat as well, so the muscles are more visible. This makes the body appear larger than it would if it were covered with a layer of fat. You can therefore "grow" even if your muscle mass is constant.

A person's performance potential is determined by their genetics. That is a fact of life. We are not all born the same. Our cardiovascular capabilities vary, as do our muscle-fiber compositions, natural hormone levels and points of muscle insertion. Our abilities to recuperate also vary. These factors can limit our ability to respond to exercise. Some people's muscles seem to grow from just a few months of training, while others train for years at the same intensity level and nothing happens. These genetic characteristics are beyond the control of human manipulation (at least for now).

At the same time, there are many environmental factors which influence muscular development:

- The strength of conviction and determination to keep to a demanding training schedule

- The ability to react positively to the physical and psychological pressures of competition

- The capacity to push through the pain barrier during training and at the competitive event.

All of these factors impact a person's success in his or her particular sport. The desire and ability to learn a skill is also environmental in nature, although our innate intelligence is, of course, genetic. This can be very important in high-skill sports like golf and tennis, while it is less so for low-skill sports like weightlifting and running. Other environmental factors we can control include nutrition and the amount of sleep we get.

Our age also influences our training abilities, although science is now finding that age is much less important a factor than originally thought. What was once considered an uncontrollable decline in sport ability now turns out to be dependent on environmental and lifestyle factors like diet and exercise. Natural athletes can improve in performance up to their 90s if the desire is there. While they might not outperform a teenager, they will nonetheless enhance their quality of life and feel those endorphins rushing through their systems. The benefits are clear.

There is no question that genetics plays a major role in sports. It has been said that if steroids had never been invented, the same people would still be winning competitions. This is largely true, although there are some individual variations in the ability to respond to steroid treatment. The most important thing to remember is that sport improves the quality of everyone's life. It is pointless to participate in a sport you don't like just because you are genetically suited for it. Likewise, it would be foolish not to enjoy a sport just because your genetics don't put you at an elite level. Natural athletes, who understand the lifelong need for an active lifestyle, should continually pursue their goals in sport and strive to achieve their greatest potential. The satisfaction they get along the way will make it all worthwhile.

CHAPTER FOUR

Man-Made Hormones

Modern medical science has created a vast array of chemical substances for the benefit of mankind. Diseases that once claimed millions of people have now been eliminated, and the lives of millions more have been prolonged by scientific discoveries. Industrious scientists have been able to unlock the secrets to the inner workings of the human body, increasing our knowledge of ourselves and the ways we interact with the environment. These discoveries have produced a great number of drugs which are effective for treating illnesses and improving the quality of life for individuals with life-threatening ailments.

Unfortunately, some athletes and coaches discovered that certain drugs, particularly hormones, could improve sports performance (at least in the short term). They began to experiment with these substances, hoping to gain an advantage over their competitors. As word got around, more and more athletes began taking drugs, until it seemed that drug use became the norm rather than the exception. This unfortunate turn of events has brought us to where we are today, with major drug abuse in sports at the international, national and even local level.

This chapter discusses two of the most widely abused drugs in sports: anabolic steroids and human growth hormone. The unique characteristics of each type of hormone are reviewed, including the short-term benefits and the long-term hazards associated with their use. Information on benefits is provided to help you understand why other less health-oriented athletes take these substances. With this knowledge you will be able to intelligently discuss hormone use with these athletes and hopefully convince them to change their ways. It is not intended in any way, shape or form to encourage experimentation with these drugs.

Anabolic Steroids

Anabolic steroids are synthetic versions of the male hormone testosterone. Originally developed in the 1940s by the German government and used experimentally on their troops during World War II, these drugs later proved valuable in speeding the recovery of persons suffering from famine and war injuries. Steroids were also used to enhance the recuperation of accident and burn victims, since they were found to stimulate tissue growth and protein synthesis. Other drugs have since been discovered which are more effective for these purposes.

Current medical uses for steroids include the treatment of anemias and other diseases. They are sometimes used with cancer radiation therapy, and have been prescribed for women with endometriosis and post-menopausal osteoperosis. Steroids have also been used in treating sexual frigidity in men (when it results from hormonal deficiencies) and for persons suffering from anorexia nervosa. Its medical use is declining, however, as better medications are developed that can treat these ailments without the side effects steroids have. This has occurred despite the fact that the dosages prescribed by doctors are miniscule compared to what athletes are taking on their own. Needless to say, this means that the negative consequences of steroid abuse by athletes will be much greater than those experienced during legitimate medical steroid use.

SHORT-TERM BENEFITS OF STEROIDS

The male hormone testosterone has many different functions in the human body. These functions are usually divided into the categories of anabolic and androgenic. Anabolic refers to the general processes of muscle growth and tissue development in the body. These are the functions that athletes seek when they take steroids. Androgenic effects are those additional functions related to the development of secondary male sex characteristics. These androgenic functions are the undesired side effects which often occur with steroid use, including acne and the usual changes which occur in males during puberty. These side effects are especially obvious in women drug users.

Steroids obviously "work" in the short term, or nobody would use them. These positive effects include enhanced recuperation, strength increases, enlarged muscle size, reduced body fat and increased vascularity. Steroids can reduce the recovery time of athletes significantly. This is due to the drug's ability to inhibit the inflammatory process. When a person exercises, one of the end results is fatigue, which, as noted earlier, produces a buildup of lactic acid in the muscle. This lactic acid is an irritant, so various tissue factors and white blood cells are sent to the muscle. These tissue factors produce inflammation which builds on itself and slows recuperation.

Anabolic steroids blunt this inflammatory response by retarding the secretions of the stress hormone cortisol after exercise. Since cortisol has a destructive effect on muscle tissue, the presence of less cortisol appears to reduce muscle damage due to exercise. Steroid use also keeps the blood level of creatine kinase (an indicator of muscle damage) from rising, suggesting enhanced recuperation. These drug-related actions allow steroid users to recover more quickly from exercise than a natural athlete, so they can return to the gym sooner for another workout.

Other positive effects of steroids include increased strength and muscle size. Both of these temporary changes are a result of the drug's ability to stimulate protein synthesis by increasing the body's retention of nitrogen, which is one of the major chemical components of protein. As was mentioned in the chapter **Muscular Development**, muscles grow because the actin and myosin myofilaments within the sarcomeres increase in size and number. Both of these myofilaments are proteins. As a result, steroids create conditions which make it easier for the myofilaments to grow, quickening the speed at which the muscles increase in size while improving their strength more rapidly than is possible naturally. Of course, this increased muscle mass and strength comes out of a bottle and goes away as soon as the drug use ceases.

Since steroids are chemically similar to male testosterone, they are processed in much the same way as the body's natural hormone. Some steroids are broken down by the liver into less toxic substances, while most are transported directly by the blood to the muscle cells. There most are transported directly by the blood to the muscle cells. There the steroid attaches to hormone receptor sites within the cell and is transported to the nucleus, where messenger RNA is formed. This RNA then leaves the nucleus and binds to the RNA in the ribosomes of the cell. These ribosomes produce the specific protein needed by the cell at that time from the available amino acids. As long as receptor sites are available, the greater the amount of steroid, the more protein is synthesized. This assumes, of course, that the cell has a need for protein as it adapts to the stresses placed on it by exercise.

It also appears that for some individuals steroids stimulate a reduction in body fat below that which could be expected from diet and exercise alone. The reasons for this are unclear, but some feel that steroids actually increase the basal metabolic rate of the user. Others speculate that steroids stimulate the growth of additional mitochondria in the cells, which play a key role in the oxidation of fats. This theory holds that the greater numbers of mitochondria allow for greater use of the fat stores for energy, eventually depleting them. This fat reduction may be the cause of the greater vascularity often seen in drug users. The increased blood pressure seen in steroid abusers may also be responsible for this vascularity.

A good deal of the weight and size gain attributed to steroids is actually added water in the muscle cells. This water retention, caused by increased glycogen and water storage, is temporary and goes away when the drug is no longer taken. That is why athletes on steroids go through those rapid weight gains and losses. Natural bodybuilders will never have to worry about these excessive fluctuations in weight, which are very taxing on the system.

It is important to remember that steroids do not directly build muscle. They "work" because they enhance the body's ability to synthesize protein, and then only if used in conjunction with a vigorous program of resistance training. A couch potato on drugs will never become Charles Atlas! The question, of course, is whether there is a better and safer way to maximize the body's ability to synthesize protein. The answer is yes! Proper nutrition and sound training techniques are the keys to growing naturally.

Many of the effects of steroids are psychological in nature. When athletes "psych" themselves into thinking they are stronger and more aggressive they actually gain measurable strength. This placebo effect is very strong and very effective. Later in this book you will read about ways to self-motivate and turn on your natural muscle machine without the use of artificial hormones.

IMPACT OF STEROIDS ON HEALTH

There are a number of health problems that can result from steroid use. Among these are cardiovascular diseases, liver damage, alterations to the reproductive system and psychological impacts. Many of the changes caused by steroids are permanent, while others are reversible once drug use ceases. They are all very real. Most of these problems, of course, are related to the dosage that is taken. Yet since most athletes use steroids without a doctor's supervision, their dosages are usually far higher than a doctor might prescribe, bringing on the dangers listed here. The best policy is to stay healthy and play it safe by never using drugs. Steroids are never good for you.

Cardiovascular problems can include heart irregularities. Steroid-induced changes in the way sugars and fats are metabolized in the body lead to heightened risks of heart attacks, strokes and buildup of plaque in the arteries (atherosclerosis). The blood's ability to clot can also be affected. Steroids also reduce the body's level of high-density lipoproteins (HDL)—the good form of cholesterol. This is one of the reasons that outwardly healthy athletes in their 20s are dropping dead of heart attacks. The body's resting blood-glucose level can be impacted as well, as can its tolerance for glucose. Both of these conditions are particularly dangerous for diabetics.

Steroids can also produce hypertension (high blood pressure) in athletes. This pressure elevation is caused by the adrenal glands, which are responsible for maintaining a proper balance of electrolytes in the body. Drugs change this balance of fluids and electrolytes, producing the puffiness frequently seen in drug users. Hypertension may also be caused by the increases in nitrogen and potassium levels that result from steroid use.

The liver is affected by steroids as well. Since it functions as the body's "sewage treatment plant," the liver is called upon to remove a variety of toxins and other poisons that pass through the system. Impaired liver functioning and even jaundice can result from high levels of steroid use. Other problems can include liver cancer, tumors and cysts. Pain in the liver and kidneys can occur at even mild dosages of the drug. This is a clear example of the body's early warning system trying to tell the mind that something is amiss. Unfortunately, all too many athletes ignore these simple signals and continue to abuse their bodies, hoping that the pain will go away or writing it off to heartburn, upset stomach or the like.

The reproductive system is also at risk when steroids are used. Because these drugs are very similar to natural testosterone, they are considered by the body to be the real thing. Therefore, since the body is a conservation-minded organism, the hypothalamus will order the testes to produce less testosterone on its own in order to maintain a constant hormone level (homeostasis) in the system. When a sufficient amount of steroids is used, the body shuts off the testes completely.

This has to be one of the major ironies of steroid use: athletes spend vast sums of money to turn off their body's own natural testosterone factory. Tangible effects from steroids (except for a temporary rebound effect after drug use ceases) occur only after the body's natural system has been completely turned off. That body-builders and other athletes get any effects from steroids at all is proof of the massive amount of drugs they are taking. What folly!

Further reproductive system impacts can include low sperm counts, shrinkage in the size of the testicles (since the body feels there is no need for them anymore) and, depending on the extent of the steroid abuse, sterility and even cancer of the testicles. While most of these impacts are reversible once steroid use stops, there have been instances where the testes shut off permanently as a result of major drug abuse. Steroids can also effect your sex drive, temporarily raising it when the drug is first used, then practically eliminating it as the body's natural hormone system shuts down. (This has been the bane of many professional football players' wives!) The extent of these changes is highly individual in nature.

Another frequent impact of steroids is the inappropriate growth of tissue around the nipple of the male breast (called gynecomastia). This is brought about by an imbalance in the body's hormone levels. While this imbalance can result from natural causes, in most cases it is the result of drug abuse. After a steroid is introduced into the body, it is either metabolized in the liver or passed through in an unaltered state. In either case it circulates throughout the body, reaching the breast, the pituitary gland and many other organs.

Some steroids effect the breast tissue directly, blocking the male hormones that inhibit the growth of the breasts. This allows the estrogens (female hormones) that exist naturally in all males to act unopposed on the breast. Other steroids act on the pituitary gland, causing the pituitary to shut down its production of LH (luteinizing hormone) and FSH (follicle-stimulating hormone). In the absence of these two hormones, the testes reduces its production of male hormone, upsetting the natural hormonal balance in the body and allowing gynecomastia to develop. After a period of drug abuse (which can range from six months to a year or more depending on the type and level of drug usage), the enlarged area around the nipple begins to harden and form scar tissue. This fibrous tissue is permanent and, once it forms, can only be removed by surgery.

The increases in muscle mass and body weight caused by steroids can also put strain on the tendons and joints in the body, creating more stress than the body can handle at that point and heightening the risk of injury. This is especially true if athletes begin steroid use as soon as they start training, since their tendons and connective tissues have not had a chance to adapt to the stresses of their sport. Moreover, in teenage men a premature hardening of the cartilage-like plates at the end of the bones can take place. These plates, which normally continue to stretch and grow throughout adolescence, suddenly harden. This stops further height increases and effectively stunts the growth of young athletes.

Steroids can also impact the immune system of users. Although it was once felt that steroids helped immune response while they were being taken, more recent research shows that steroid users have lower levels of immunoglobin proteins, which guard against infections from viruses, bacteria and fungi. This may be the reason some athletes are afflicted with colds and viruses (although overtraining and the lowered resistance that comes with it surely play a role as well).

Another frequent consequence of steroid use is acne. This results from an overactivation of the sebaceous glands in the skin, which produce oil and create unsightly pimples. Many teenagers get acne during puberty when their natural hormone levels begin to rise. Steroid use adds even more hormone into the athlete's body, often producing serious outbreaks of acne. Natural acne, of course, usually disappears by the time an individual reaches the age of 20 or so. Much older athletes with acne problems are almost always taking steroids.

The effects of steroids on women are even more severe, since natural testosterone levels in women are very low (less than 5 percent of the average man's level). Frequent effects include a lowering of the voice, increased facial and body hair, reduced breast size (although dieting also assists in this process), acne, genital enlargement, altered menstrual cycles and, in some severe cases, breast cancer and sterility.

While some of these changes are reversible, many are unfortunately permanent. As with any nonessential drug, steroid use should especially be avoided during pregnancy and while the child is being breast fed.

Psychological changes caused by steroids can play havoc with a person's social life and work. Abusing athletes are frequently subject to violent mood swings with increased hostility and aggressive behavior. Paranoia and disruptions to sleep patterns can occur. Psychological addiction to the drug can also take place, with the classic patterns of self-denial ("I'm not hooked; I can get off this stuff any time I like").

Depression often occurs when an athlete stops using drugs. The person's self-esteem frequently decreases, as does the desire to train. Intensity levels drop. These changes can last for weeks or even months, depending on the length and quantity of usage. If the person has tried to "go off" before, the realization that bad times lie ahead can lead to rationalizations about the continual use of drugs. This can be very dangerous because non-stop drug use does not give the body time to recuperate and heal the damage caused by steroids. Many of the horror stories that you hear about steroid use involve people who have became so addicted to steroids they can't even stop for a month or two every once in a while to give their bodies time to repair. It seems so shortsighted.

There are a wide variety of steroids on the market. Athletes try to choose those drugs with the greatest anabolic characteristics combined with the least number of androgenic side effects. This can be difficult, because many of the drugs with the greatest anabolic properties also have the most androgenic impacts. There is also a great deal of misinformation about steroids, especially for those athletes who purchase drugs from uninformed persons like gym owners or friends.

It is also hard to tell legitimate drugs from black market products. Athletes may get accurate information about a particular drug, yet wind up purchasing something that is totally different. If they are lucky, these black market drugs will be useless, inert material like vegetable oil. Less fortunate people may wind up with infections, especially at the point of injection (myositis), and organ damage. Also, some athletes use veterinary steroids either by choice or chance. This creates even greater danger, since products for animals do not have to meet the health standards established for human drugs. The higher level of permitted impurities can cause health problems in certain instances.

Except for acne, the negative impacts of steroids are internal and therefore not recognizable to the average person. Since athletes often choose steroids for maximum size and strength gains, they may then rationalize any pains or negative sensations in their bodies. Only blood tests can provide an indication of the real strains that steroids place on the athlete's organs and biochemistry.

Human Growth Hormone

In the past few years another hormone has appeared on the athletic scene: human growth hormone, or hGH. As was noted in the chapter **Muscular Development**, growth hormone is produced naturally by the pituitary gland and is essential for muscle growth. Available from human pituitary extracts and through genetic engineering, it has been a godsend for children with deficient pituitaries, allowing them to grow to more usual heights. Lately, however, healthy athletes have been injecting supplemental growth hormone in an attempt to produce even greater gains in muscle strength and size.

SHORT-TERM BENEFITS OF SUPPLEMENTAL GROWTH HORMONE

Some athletes who have taken supplemental growth hormone report increased muscle mass from its use. This appears to result from an increase in the formation of collagen (connective tissue) surrounding the muscle fibers and not from the creation of additional myofilaments within the muscle cell itself. Increased protein synthesis has been reported, however, in some studies. Cartilage growth is also stimulated by hGH.

Supplemental growth hormone can also reduce the fat stores of the body by increasing the amount of fatty acids taken from adipose tissue. These fatty acids then circulate in the blood, where they can be used for energy. HGH is also said to alter the body's metabolism in favor of fatty acids, allowing more of the glycogen and protein in the muscles to be used for anabolic purposes. Increased insulin production has also been reported.

It should be noted that many athletes do not experience any benefit at all from supplemental growth hormone. While it is still not known why this occurs, individual variations in natural hormone levels may be part of the answer. There are also several other naturally occurring hormones in the body which act to keep hGH within proper limits. It may be that these hormones neutralize the supplemental hGH in many instances.

Since growth hormone injections are extremely expensive (costing several thousand dollars for a two-month administration), it seems clear that most athletes are throwing their money away. Imagine if they had spent all those dollars on improving their diets or for nutritional supplementation. Surely the long-term results would have been greater!

NEGATIVE IMPACTS OF SUPPLEMENTAL GROWTH HORMONE

The negative effects of supplemental hGH are only now becoming clear. The most serious result is acromegaly—an irreversible disease that results in thickening of the bones and organs. This thickening occurs throughout the body but is most visible in the hands, feet and face. The skin becomes very coarse, giving it the consistency of raw leather at high dosages. The aging process accelerates as well.

Big Foot is the legendary example of a person with acromegalic features. Many persons who are naturally afflicted with acromegaly (due to hyperactive pituitaries) develop arthritis and diabetes, and have very short life spans. It seems reasonable to assume that athletes who use supplemental growth hormone will become afflicted with these problems later in their lives. Moreover, if the hGH is from extracts of human pituitaries there is a danger of contamination, infection and antibody formation. These dangers are multiplied if the athlete resorts to primate growth hormone.

Properly nourished and stimulated through exercise, the body is capable of great feats of physical growth on its own. Artificial hormones are not even needed. We have seen the dangers and potential problems that accompany the use of steroids and growth hormone. The lesson is clear: artificial hormones are shortcuts that hurt YOU in the end. Train for your health. That's the biggest prize of all!

CHAPTER FIVE

Proteins, Carbohydrates And Fats

Natural athletes need to pay close attention to diet and nutrition. While people who use drugs are able to achieve temporary gains in muscle size and strength through chemical manipulation, the natural athlete can reach his or her ultimate potential only through a scientifically based diet program that provides the body with the nutrients it needs.

In this chapter the three macronutrients (proteins, carbohydrates and fats) are discussed, while in the following chapter topics such as fiber, cholesterol, vitamins, minerals and water are analyzed. Each discussion includes the Dietary Guidelines which relate to that nutrient. These Guidelines provide general rules and suggestions that you can use to improve your personal diet program. Chapters Seven and Eight (**Tips for Home-Cooked Meals** and **Tips for Eating Out**) then show how the Dietary Guidelines can be applied to each of the meals you eat during the day, whether you eat them at home or in a restaurant. Incorporating these Guidelines into your diet will improve your performance as an athlete and will enhance the way you look.

Sometimes a natural athlete will look at the physiques of high-level bodybuilders and reach the conclusion that drugs are the sole reason that his or her body looks different from those of the top names in that sport. While drugs obviously provide short-term "help" (although at a price), it is overly simplistic to write off all of these differences to steroids. Diet and nutrition play major roles in muscular development. In fact, without proper diet it is impossible to reach your personal best—with or without chemical assistance. Proper nutrition is essential to achieving your goals in any sport, and writing off everything to drugs is the easy way out. You *can* reach your optimal performance level without drugs, but only if you pay close attention to the Dietary Guidelines and thoroughly incorporate them into your diet—day in and day out. This will provide you with the raw materials your body needs to excel in the sport of your choice. The rest is up to you.

Protein

Protein is an essential nutrient for natural athletes. There is some protein in every single cell of the human body. Brain cells, for example, are 10 percent protein while red blood and muscle cells contain as much as 20 percent protein. There are many different types of protein as well. While athletes normally focus on the proteins used for muscle contraction, there are literally thousands of different proteins throughout the body. All in all, protein makes up nearly 15 percent of a person's bodyweight—more than any other substance except water.

These proteins have a wide range of functions. They are required for the growth and development of every tissue in the body. Proteins are present in the cell membrane and the internal cellular material, including the nucleus. The hair, tendons, ligaments, skin and nails are all specialized kinds of structural proteins. Proteins are used to form some 2,000 different enzymes, which speed up chemical reactions throughout the body. They are also needed to form most hormones, including insulin and growth hormone. Proteins are contained in the blood as well, where they have several crucial functions, such as blood clotting. They also play an important role in maintaining the proper chemical balance of the body's fluids. This is particularly important during exercise, when lactic acid is produced in great quantities.

AMINO ACIDS

All of these different proteins are manufactured by the body from the raw materials in the dietary protein you eat. These raw materials are referred to as amino acids—the "building blocks" for the human body. There are 20 amino acids in foods: alanine, arginine, asparagine, aspartic acid, cystine, glutamine, glutamic acid, glycine, histidine, isoleucine, leucine, lysine, methionine, phenylalanine, proline, serine, threonine, tryptophan, tyrosine and valine.

In the body, dietary protein is broken down into these amino acids, which are then reconstructed in a variety of ways depending on the needs of the body at that time. The amino acids in a protein are linked together much like the beads on a necklace. The order that these proteins have on the "necklace" is very important. Even when two proteins contain the same amino acids, if their order on the "necklace" is different, the proteins will have distinct characteristics and functions.

Twelve of these amino acids (eleven in children) can be manufactured by the body whenever they are needed. They are called nonessential amino acids. This does not mean they are unimportant, however. The term nonessential signifies that the body can synthesize them from compounds normally present in the body at a rate equal to the body's need for them. The other eight amino acids (nine in children) are called essential because they must be supplied by the diet. These essential amino acids are: isoleucine, leucine, lysine, methionine, phenylalanine, threonine, tryptophan and valine. Histidine is the ninth essential amino acid for children. It is also essential for some elderly persons who experience a lot of stress.

Foods can be classified by the quality of the amino acids contained in them. It doesn't particularly matter whether an amino acid comes from a plant or animal source, since there is only one naturally occurring form of each amino acid. (Plants form their amino acids from the nitrogen in the soil, while animals get their aminos from the plant and animal proteins they consume.) What is important is the combination and proportion of different amino acids in the foods we eat.

Foods which contain amino acids in the right quantities and ratios to support tissue growth and repair are called complete proteins. Eating the right amount of these foods assures you an adequate supply of all of the essential amino acids. Incomplete proteins, on the other hand, are those foods which lack one or more of the essential amino acids. If incomplete proteins are eaten by themselves as the protein source, it is possible to have a protein deficiency even if the total quantity of protein eaten is sufficient for your needs.

This is because the deficient amino acid becomes a limiting factor for the protein production process, effectively stopping protein synthesis even though all of the other amino acids are available in adequate quantities. While severe protein deficiencies are rare in the world's industrialized countries, a deficiency of protein can stunt the growth of children and cause weakness, depression and low energy levels in adults. It can also reduce the effectiveness of the immune system and slow recovery from diseases and injuries.

As a result, it is very important for natural athletes to consume complete proteins in your diet. This can be done by eating proteins that are complete in and of themselves, or by eating two protein sources which together contain all of the essential amino acids. Foods that are individually complete include eggs, milk, meat, fish and poultry. Of all these foods, eggs have the best combination of amino acids. They have therefore been used as the foundation for a system of measuring protein quality called Biologic Value. As can be seen in Table 1, eggs have a biologic value of 100. Milk is ranked at 91, while most meats are a bit less at around 80. All vegetable sources of protein rank even lower due to their deficiencies in certain amino acids.

TABLE 1
BIOLOGIC VALUE

Protein Source	Biologic Value
Eggs	100
Milk	91
Beef	80
Fish	78
Soya protein	74
Rice	59
Wheat	54
Peanuts	43
Dry Beans	34
Potato	34

Biologic value is the best system for evaluating protein quality because humans were used in the studies that led to the development of this system. However, another system—the Protein Efficiency Ratio (PER)—is sometimes used. While PER gives relatively similar rankings for different protein sources, the studies on which it is based were performed on animals. As a result, it is not as precise as biologic value.

While most people in the industrialized nations of the world get the majority of their protein from animal sources, it is possible to get adequate protein from vegetable products if the foods are eaten in the right combinations. Basically, beans or nuts should be eaten with grains like corn, wheat or rice. Tofu, which is made from soybeans, should also be eaten with grains. These combinations create complete protein foods by combining one food deficient in a particular amino acid with another food which contains it. For example, beans do not have methionine, although they contain good amounts of lysine and tryptophan. Corn, on the other hand, has plenty of methionine, but is lacking in lysine and tryptophan. Together these foods make a complete protein. There really is something to the traditional Mexican diet of beans and corn tortillas!

PROTEIN REQUIREMENTS

One of the main questions that natural athletes ask is how much protein they should consume. This topic has been the subject of endless debate among nutritionists and coaches, who have come up with recommendations that can vary by as much as 100 percent! The Recommended Daily Allowance (RDA) for protein has been established by the U.S. Government at 0.8 grams per kilogram of body-weight, which is equal to 0.36 grams per pound. (The RDA for adolescents is 0.9 grams per kilo, equal to 0.42 grams per pound.)

While some nutritionists maintain that this is a liberal allowance which provides enough protein for athletes as well, most sports physicians feel that the body's demands for protein increase significantly due to training. Several studies have shown that natural athletes with vigorous training schedules can require up to double the RDA to maintain positive nitrogen balance—from 1.5 to 1.8 grams per kilo (0.68 to 0.82 grams per pound) depending on their activity level.

Using this guideline, a 200-pound athlete would need from 136 to 164 grams of protein daily, which would equal approximately 20 percent of the athlete's total caloric intake. The exact percentage, of course, will vary with the athlete's short-term goals (weight reduction for a competition, "bulking up", etc.) and the resulting amounts of carbohydrate and fat in the diet.

You need to eat an adequate amount of complete protein every day, even on the days you don't exercise. The body uses protein continuously to provide the raw materials for muscle growth, repair and maintenance. When more protein is consumed than the body needs at a particular moment, the body is said to be in positive nitrogen balance. If you don't give your body the quantity and quality of protein it needs, however, it will be in negative nitrogen balance. In this situation it will get the protein it requires from the liver and muscles. This will result in a loss in muscle size and strength—hardly what a natural athlete wants!

Some natural athletes feel that they need to eat more protein than people who use "protein-sparing" steroids. The concept that steroids "spare" protein, however, is not really correct. While steroids stimulate protein synthesis and increase nitrogen retention in the short term, they do so only in the presence of adequate amino acid supplies. Yet since steroids speed up the anabolic process, they actually require more amino acids as raw material than would normally be needed for muscle development during a given time period. This means that the protein requirements of drug-free athletes are actually lower than those of steroid users. The 1.5 to 1.8 grams per kilo guideline mentioned earlier is adequate to assure positive nitrogen balance under normal conditions. It even provides a bit of extra protein as an "insurance policy" for those days when your protein requirement goes up due to stress, extra-heavy training or other factors.

It is possible, however, to wind up with a negative nitrogen balance even at these protein levels if you do not consume enough carbohydrates. This can occur during the carbohydrate-depletion diets that are sometimes used prior to competitions. It often occurs as well during long-distance marathon racing. When your body needs energy and does not have sufficient carbohydrates to meet its needs, it uses up all the glycogen it has available and then converts the protein in its liver and muscle stores into energy. Since the demand for protein in this case exceeds the amount of protein consumed, the body will be in negative nitrogen balance. This also results in a loss in muscle mass, as the body literally eats away at itself to provide the nutrients it needs. It is also important to note that excessive protein consumption puts strains on the liver and kidneys as they are forced to break down and reconstruct the components of the protein you consume. It's also very expensive.

PROTEIN ASSIMILATION

The process of breaking down protein begins in the mouth, where the bits of food are mixed with saliva. In the stomach, the long chains of amino acids are broken down into smaller chains with the help of the enzyme pepsin. These smaller chains are further broken down in the small intestine into single amino acids and short chains of amino acids called dipeptides and tripeptides. The bonds connecting the amino acid chains are called peptide bonds.

The single amino acids and peptide chains pass through the wall of the small intestine and enter the bloodstream, which transports them eventually to the liver. In the liver, these amino acids can be converted into nonessential amino acids, broken down for energy or used to make more complex proteins. They can also pass unchanged through the liver and continue to circulate in the blood.

What actually happens to a particular amino acid or peptide chain depends on the needs of the body at that time. However, if it is not needed by the body for anabolic purposes, it will eventually be broken down by a process called protein catabolism. During catabolism, the nitrogen in the amino acid is stripped away in the liver and converted to an ammonia-like substance called urea. This urea is then excreted from the body through the urine, feces or sweat. The remaining carbon skeleton is either used immediately for energy or is stored as fat. It will *not* be converted to muscle protein and will not improve your sports performance in any way.

As a result, excess protein consumption should be avoided, even during carbohydrate-depletion diets. The urea produced from the breakdown of the extra protein is toxic to the system, and the energy produced from the carbon skeletons can be more easily obtained by eating carbohydrates. There is simply no reason to take in more protein than your body needs.

AMINO ACID SUPPLEMENTS

Another frequently asked question about protein deals with amino acid supplements. These supplements have been promoted by some as magic pills with great powers. Unfortunately, they are nothing of the kind. Amino acid tablets are nothing more, and nothing less, than protein that has been predigested (hydrolyzed) by an industrial process. While the precise formulation varies with the brand name, most provide all of the essential amino acids in proportions that approximate those needed by the body. They therefore offer a way to consume protein without the fat (and all the bother) that comes along with cooking and eating most protein sources.

There have been studies which indicate that crystalline free-form amino acids (the types that come in powder form or in gelatin-coated capsules) have been so overly processed that they cannot be fully assimilated by the body. According to these studies, the body is designed to assimilate the dipeptides and tripeptides that the digestive system mainly produces from the foods we eat. These peptides are the same components which are supplied by peptide-bond amino acids. Assimilation is therefore greater with peptide-bond aminos than it is with the individual amino acids provided by the crystalline supplements. There can also be more digestive upset from these metallic-tasting crystalline products. They cost more than the peptide-bond supplements as well. So if you are going to use amino acid supplements, stick with the peptide-bond formulas.

A few words of caution, however. There are two forms of each amino acid produced by the hydrolysis process—the D-form and the L-form. L-form amino acids are the type which your body can absorb and utilize for its protein requirements. D-form amino-acid molecules, on the other hand, are the mirror image of the L-form. The reversed shape of their molecules keeps them from being utilized by the body. In fact, D-form aminos actually compete with the L-forms for the limited number of transport sites available to pick up amino acids in the body—reducing your effective protein intake.

Consuming D-form aminos, therefore, is worse than taking no amino-acid supplements at all. Since it is much more expensive to use only L-form aminos, any producer of amino acids will advertise this fact on their labels (since the price of their product will be higher than a comparable product with D-forms in it). So if you see amino acids for sale that do not say L-form, such as L-Lysine, put them back on the shelf. Don't be suckered into thinking that you can save money by taking a few more to even things out. Use L-form amino acids or nothing at all!

Amino acid tablets are expensive—far more expensive than the foods they are made from. (Most are prepared using casein, a milk protein.) So unless you have money to burn, you should use them only when they offer you a particular advantage. This advantage comes before and after the workout, since their predigested form allows them to enter the bloodstream quicker than a regular protein.

Most protein sources, such as eggs and dairy products, take two to three hours to reach the bloodstream. Meats can take up to four hours. Yet after a workout you need to supply your muscles with amino acids for protein synthesis as soon as you possibly can. Amino acid tablets can come to the rescue, entering your bloodstream in 15 to 20 minutes. This speeds your recuperation process by several hours a day, which can add up to significantly more muscle growth over time. Taking a few amino acid tablets before your workout will also provide a quick source of protein to keep your blood, liver and muscle stores from depleting quite so much. They also help to maintain your blood-sugar level.

If you can afford 10 tablets per day, take four before and six after the workout. If 20 tablets are within your budget, do eight before and 12 after. No more than 20 are ever needed. The rest of the day and on days you don't workout you should eat regular protein sources at your meals. This way you will spread out your protein consumption over the day, maintain a more constant amino-acid level in the blood, save money and make your diet a lot more interesting than it would be just swallowing tablets.

DIETARY GUIDELINES

Here are some Dietary Guidelines for protein:

Count your protein consumption every day to make sure you get enough. Your body needs amino acids daily, even on the days you don't work out. The only way you can be sure you get enough protein is by counting the amount you take in every day. This is easy once you get the hang of it. There are several nutritional almanacs and books available which list the protein content of most foods. Make a note of the number of grams of protein per ounce in the meats, fish and lowfat cheeses you like. Then weigh your foods (or note the weight on the packages you bought at the supermarket) and figure out the total amount of protein you consume per day. A gram of protein has four calories.

Try to keep this amount fairly constant, without major dips or peaks. Your need for protein does not vary that much from one day to the next, and it is pointless to go into protein catabolism on the days you eat too much protein, only to have your body turn around and take it from your liver and muscles on the days you eat too little. Figure out the amount of protein you need based on your weight and activity level and consume it every day. This will maximize your anabolic processes and stimulate the greatest amount of muscle strength and growth.

Divide your total protein requirement into several portions. As noted earlier, the body needs amino acids throughout the day. Since there is only a limited protein storage capacity in the liver, the only way to assure a positive nitrogen balance all day long is to eat relatively small amounts of protein at several meals during the day. Rather than having all of your protein at dinner, eat more for breakfast and lunch. Then you can have a smaller portion in the evening. You could also try to eat snacks with protein in them, such as nonfat yogurt. This will maintain a more even level of amino acids in your blood throughout the day and will assure that the protein in your muscles is only used to make them bigger and stronger.

Pay attention to protein quality. Remember that the body can't produce the essential amino acids. If your diet does not supply the body with all of the amino acids it needs for creating a particular protein, protein synthesis will not take place. The best way to make sure you get enough high-quality protein is to only count the protein contained in eggs, meat, fish, poultry and milk products as part of your daily protein intake. You can also include the protein in certain vegetable foods, but only if you eat them in the combinations that will make their total amino-acid content complete. Otherwise it's best to ignore the protein in them altogether.

Carbohydrates

Carbohydrates are the best source of energy fuel for the body. Although proteins can be converted into energy when there are no carbohydrates available, carbohydrates offer the most efficient and least taxing way for the body to get the energy it needs. There are 4 calories in each gram of "carb." These carbs provide the energy for muscular contraction and all physical exertion. This is especially important for natural athletes who have long training sessions or who perform endurance-type activities like marathon racing. Without a continual source of carbohydrates the body's primary energy engine grinds to a halt. This can mean the difference between victory and defeat in an athletic competition.

Carbohydrates are an essential part of a healthy diet for many reasons. Adequate carbohydrates in the diet allow all of the dietary protein you consume to be used for its primary purpose of tissue growth and development. For this reason, carbohydrates are said to have a protein-sparing effect. A diet that is high in carbohydrates will also be relatively low in fats, which helps to prevent heart disease and other health problems.

The brain and central nervous system rely on the carbohydrate glucose to function normally, and during anaerobic activities like weightlifting only blood glucose and glycogen (the storage form of glucose) can be used to generate the energy molecule ATP. While this glucose is sometimes produced indirectly from proteins, the vast majority of it comes from carbohydrate metabolism. Furthermore, even though the muscles and liver have a glycogen storage of 400 to 500 grams (about one pound), this limited capacity can be depleted by only a few hours of training, depending on your sport and intensity level. When glycogen stores are used up, fatigue sets in and exercise must stop. Marathon runners call this "hitting the wall." It is therefore essential that an adequate supply of carbohydrates be available at all times for maximum performance. During light and moderate exercise, when more aerobic energy production is involved, carbohydrates still provide over half of the body's total energy requirements. (The rest comes from the fatty acids in the body's fat stores.)

It also appears that carbohydrates are needed to fully process dietary fats for energy. When adequate carbohydrates are not available, the body only partially metabolizes fats, resulting in an acidic condition known as ketosis. The body can literally run out of fuel even if fat calories are theoretically available. This explains why "zero-carb" diets (when only fats and proteins are consumed) can cause athletes to run out of energy and feel "brain-dead" even when eating a moderate level of non-carbohydrate calories. If you have ever considered doing a zero-carb diet to make weight for a wrestling or bodybuilding competition, forget it. This diet puts your body in shock and can actually lead to fat retention as the body's protective mechanisms respond to what they perceive as a famine. Hypoglycemia and its accompanying dizziness, hunger and weakness can also occur. The best way to lose fat is to continue eating carbohydrates and slowly reduce your total caloric intake while exercising. This theory of weight reduction is discussed in **More on Diet and Nutrition**.

To assure optimal athletic performance at least 60 percent of the calories in your diet should come from carbohydrate sources. If you have an intense training schedule or are an endurance athlete, the percentage should be even higher—70 to 80 percent. This will permit the greatest storage of glycogen in your liver and muscles and improve your ability to exercise at the intensity needed to be a natural champion. Studies have shown that increasing the percentage of carbohydrates in the diet from 50 to 70 percent can double the storage of muscle glycogen. This can easily be the difference between winning and second place. Bodybuilders can get larger muscle mass through the manipulation of muscle glycogen levels as well, since a gram of glycogen combines with 2.7 grams of water. This increase in muscle fullness can be a major factor in deciding who comes out on top in a competition. The added muscle volume can also make your skin tighter and improve vascularity, giving you an extra plus.

THE THREE TYPES OF CARBOHYDRATES

There are actually several different types of carbohydrates: monosaccharides, disaccharides and polysaccharides. Monosaccharides and disaccharides are frequently referred to as simple sugars, while the polysaccharides are often called complex carbohydrates. The difference among the three kinds lies in the number of molecules that are linked together.

Monosaccharides, as their name implies, are made up of one molecule of sugar. The most common monosaccharides are glucose and fructose, although galactose also contains a single molecule. Glucose is the type of sugar that the body eventually processes all other sugars into. It is glucose that circulates in the blood to feed the brain and the muscles. For this reason it is often called blood sugar. Fructose is the type of sugar found in most fruits.

Disaccharides contain two molecules of sugar which are linked together. The three most common types are: sucrose, lactose and maltose. These disaccharides are made from the bonding of two monosaccharides. For example, sucrose (table sugar) is actually a molecule of fructose tied to a molecule of glucose. Lactose, found in milk and sometimes called milk sugar, is formed by linking up glucose and galactose. Maltose is formed by combining two molecules of glucose.

The most complex forms of carbohydrates are polysaccharides. Polysaccharides are made from the linking together of many different monosaccharides, forming long chains of molecules. The three types of polysaccharides are starch, glycogen and cellulose.

Starches are found in many grains and in vegetables, especially potatoes. In fact, starch is the way that plants store their carbohydrates. Glycogen, on the other hand, is how glucose is stored in animals.

Cellulose is a form of carbohydrate that makes up much of the physical structure in plants. It cannot be used by humans as an energy source, however, because our digestive systems are unable to break down the bonds that hold this polysaccharide together. Cellulose has value as fiber, however. The need for fiber in the diet is discussed in the next chapter.

In the stomach and small intestine all three types of carbohydrates are broken down into the monosaccharides glucose, fructose and galactose. This allows them to pass through the intestinal wall, so they can be assimilated into the blood stream. These nutrients are then transported to the liver, where fructose and galactose are converted into glucose. All carbohydrates, therefore, are reduced to glucose by the time they leave the liver.

The liver can do one of several things with this glucose. It can store it in the liver as glycogen or it can release it back into the blood for use as energy. When the body has more blood glucose than it needs for immediate energy, it takes the extra glucose and converts it into muscle glycogen. It is only after the glycogen stores are filled up that the body takes the remaining blood glucose and stores it as fat. The actual blood-sugar level is controlled by the pancreas, which releases the hormones insulin and glucagon whenever needed to keep blood glucose within its proper limits.

THE GLYCEMIC INDEX

It was once felt that all simple sugars were digested and assimilated rapidly by the body, producing a large increase in blood-sugar level and soon afterward a rise in insulin release. Complex carbohydrates, on the other hand, were thought to assimilate more slowly, resulting in less rapid changes in blood-sugar and insulin levels. Research has shown that this view of digestion and assimilation is too simplistic.

While there is a great deal of variation in the time it takes for particular foods to be absorbed into the bloodsteam, factors other than the structure of the sugar are involved. On the next page is a table which shows the glycemic index for many common foods. As you can see, some sugary products, like a candy bar, are actually converted into blood glucose at a rate slower than potatoes. Rice can cause a greater rise in blood sugar than fruits like apples and oranges, while pure fructose will stimulate less insulin production than spaghetti! Foods with fat in them are always assimilated more slowly than pure carbohydrate foods.

TABLE 2
GLYCEMIC INDEX FOR SELECTED FOODS

Food	Glycemic Index	Food	Glycemic Index
Breakfast Cereals		**Legumes**	
All-bran	51	Beans, baked	40
Cornflakes	80	Beans, butter	36
Oatmeal	54	Beans, kidney	29
Shredded Wheat	67	Chick-peas	36
		Green peas	51
Dairy Products		Lentils	29
Ice Cream	36	Soybeans	15
Milk, skim	32		
Milk, whole	34	**Miscellaneous**	
Yogurt	36	Honey	87
		Mars Bar	68
Fruits		Peanuts	13
Apples	39	Potato Chips	51
Bananas	62		
Oranges	40	**Sugars**	
Orange Juice	46	Fructose	20
Raisins	64	Glucose	100
		Maltose	105
Grains		Sucrose	59
Bread, wheat	72		
Bread, white	69	**Vegetables**	
Rice, brown	66	Beets	64
Rice, white	72	Carrots	92
Spaghetti, wheat	42	Corn-on-cob	59
Spaghetti, white	50	Potato	70
		Yam	51

The glycemic index can be of great value to natural athletes who are loading up on carbohydrates for a competition. Since foods with a lower glycemic index are assimilated at a slower rate, they can provide a more steady supply of energy than the higher glycemic index foods, which are more likely to provide the "sugar rush" associated with sweets. Lower index foods will also result in higher muscle glycogen levels and less storage of the glucose as fat. Marathon runners and bicycle racers should therefore eat foods with low glycemic indices prior to their competitions. This would also be true for bodybuilders who face a long day of judging but who want to keep their stomachs flat. At the same time, bodybuilders who have overdieted may lack vascularity before going on stage. The quick surge in carbohydrate levels provided by high glycemic-index foods may be just what they need to improve their appearance rapidly.

It should be stressed that when foods of different types are mixed together the glycemic index can be altered so much that it loses its value as a tool. This occurs when you eat your normal everyday meal of proteins, carbohydrates and fats. Therefore, natural athletes who are not competing in the immediate future do not need to concern themselves with the glycemic index. It is always a good idea, however, to get the bulk of your calories from complex carbohydrates for their greater nutritional and fiber content.

SUGAR: HOW BAD IS IT?

There is a lot of misinformation going around about sugar (sucrose, actually.) Some people claim that it is plain ole carbohydrate just like a potato, while other people avoid it like the plague, only to eat honey or molasses. It turns out that neither of these "facts" is true. There are major differences in the glycemic index of various foods, which affect their assimilation times and their impacts on insulin levels. There are also widely varying nutrient values in different foods, which play (or should play) a major role in the selection of foods for the diet.

It has been estimated that 25 percent of the calories consumed in the United States are actually sucrose. The average American now consumes over 120 pounds of sugar each year! Studies have shown that large amounts of sucrose in the diet can produce obesity, which can lead to diabetes and an increased probability of glucose intolerance. The consumption of large amounts of empty calories in sucrose makes it easier to put on weight because sucrose-rich foods are long on calories and short on volume. The person therefore eats more calories than normal to fill their stomach. Relying on these empty calories can result in nutritional deficiencies even at high calorie levels. There has even been research that connects high sucrose intake to increased cholesterol and blood triglyceride (fat) levels, as well as heart disease and, of course, tooth decay. So excess sucrose consumption is definitely not a good thing.

By the same token, the end product of all the different carbohydrates we eat, including all the sugars, is glucose—blood glucose. The polysaccharides require more processing in the digestive tract to break down their complex molecules into glucose than the disaccharides or monosaccharides, but the final result is always the same. So there's no reason to get paranoid about sugar in modest amounts. The main reasons you should eat the lower glycemic-index foods are their greater nutritional values and the reduced impact they have on insulin production.

Another factor to consider: what most people think of as "sweets" are actually concoctions with lots of fat in them as well as sugar. Chocolate cake, for example, has plenty of fat in the icing and cake along with piles of sugar. This fat content makes a major contribution to the calorie count of the dessert and in excess can contribute to coronary problems. In fact, the fat is as bad or worse for you than the sugar is. This is not in defense of sugar, mind you. It's just that people need to look at the total composition of the foods they eat, especially the desserts. There are frozen desserts now in the supermarkets which use artificial sweeteners but have lots of fat in them. What sense does this make? You're better off with a smaller portion of dessert, or better yet, a piece of fruit.

Some people feel that certain types of simple sugars are better for you than others. To some extent this is true. Fructose has a much lower glycemic index than sucrose, so it has less impact on insulin levels. It is also sweeter than sucrose, so you can get an equivalent amount of sweetness for fewer calories. These are the reasons that health food stores frequently substitute fructose for sucrose. It is wrong, however, to think that fructose is a sugar substitute. It *is* sugar—better than sucrose, perhaps, but still sugar.

As for all of the other forms of sugar, there really is no difference between them. Molasses is a byproduct of the sugar cane production process. It doesn't look like table sugar, but that's about it. Brown sugar and turbinado sugar are sucrose with a bit of molasses thrown in, while powdered sugar is plain table sugar finely ground up. Even maple sugar is predominately sucrose. Only honey is somewhat different, since it is a combination of fructose, glucose and water. Still, there is no scientific evidence that the body digests honey any differently than sucrose. If you like its taste, then have some, but there's no reason to think that it's any better for you. In fact, it can rot your teeth quicker than sucrose. The choice depends on your personal taste.

DIETARY GUIDELINES

Here are some Dietary Guidelines for carbohydrates:

Spread out your carbohydrate consumption. The best way to maintain a relatively constant blood-glucose level is to eat carbohydrates at four or five small meals throughout the day. Since the body has a significant storage capacity for glucose in its glycogen stores, it is not as critical to spread out your carbohydrates as it is to evenly proportion your protein consumption. Still, it is never a good idea to starve all day long and then stuff yourself at dinner. This starve and stuff cycle can lead to major swings in your glucose levels, requiring the intervention of great quantities of insulin and later glucagon. While most healthy persons can tolerate these fluctuations, they have to put some wear and tear on the body. High blood-glucose levels can also increase the uptake of glucose into the fat cells.

Starve and stuff can also put your mind through major up- and down-swings. You can get depressed and moody when your blood-sugar level drops. Eating gives you a needed "rush" as your glucose level shoots up, but eventually the inevitable letdown comes. Some people are so afflicted with these mood swings that they become addicted to high glycemic-index foods that can satisfy their cravings quickly. The best way to make sure this never happens to you is to spread out your carbohydrate intake among several meals.

Also, remember that large carbohydrate meals can somewhat reduce the secretion of growth hormone from the pituitary. (This is especially important for our pre-workout meal and dinner.) Yet another reason to have four or five smaller meals throughout the day!

Eat mostly complex carbohydrates. Foods which are lower on the glycemic index assimilate more slowly and cause less radical swings in your blood-glucose and insulin levels. Although there are exceptions, as a general rule complex carbohydrates have lower values on the glycemic index than the simple sugars. Complex carbs also have a lot more nutritional value than the empty calories found in sugary products. So try to eat complex carbohydrates as frequently as possible. Of course, everyone has cravings for sweets every once in a while. And every once in a while there is nothing wrong with giving in to those cravings. Just try to make these splurges the exception and not the rule.

Don't eat sucrose before your workout. Sometimes natural athletes think that eating sugary snacks before a workout will provide a quick energy boost and increase their energy level throughout the workout. While foods that are predominately sucrose do assimilate quickly, they also stimulate the release of insulin to counteract the rapid rise in blood-sugar level. So much insulin is released, in fact, that the level of blood sugar ends up being too low, requiring the release of glucagon to raise the level back to where it should be. During this period of overreaction, your energy level will be lower than normal, not greater. Your pre-workout meal should therefore consist of a fructose-based product or, better yet, complex carbohydrates. This will provide a much better source of prolonged energy throughout your workout.

Consider food combinations. While all humans have digestive systems that operate in much the same way, it appears that some individuals are more sensitive to the mixing of different food groups than others. In particular, it seems that combining fruits with complex carbohydrates and proteins in the same meal can create digestive disorders, especially gas, in certain persons. The greater the quantity of fruit mixed in, the greater the discomfort.

You have probably heard the adage "eat melons alone or leave them alone." This is because they decompose very quickly in the stomach and can cause gas due to certain enzymes which they contain. It appears that most acidic fruits cause this same problem to a lesser extent. The problem is magnified when complex carbohydrates and proteins are added to the mixture, since these foods require different digestive enzymes than fruits do. When both types of enzymes are present in the stomach at the same time, they can work against each other. The extent to which noticeable gas and digestive discomfort are produced appears to depend on the individual.

The only way to find out if food combining will make a difference for you is to experiment with it. Try eating your fruits only as snacks or at a separate meal. Don't have fruit or sweets for dessert immediately after your meal. This includes fruit juices and sodas. Wait a while to let your dinner digest before digging into that fruit cocktail. Some persons claim that food combining has improved the digestion of their meals. Others say it has even enhanced the assimilation of their food and eliminated bouts with diarrhea. Still others feel the concept has no merit at all. So find out for yourself. You have nothing to lose, and possibly something to gain.

Fats

There is a great deal of confusion about the proper role for fats in the diet. Sometimes natural athletes are told that fats serve no useful purpose and should be completely eliminated from the diet. At the same time, the average American consumes over 40 percent of their calories in the form of fat. The situation is made even more complex by the various types of fat, some of which are promoted as being good while others are on the list of things to avoid. Yet by following a few simple rules it is easy to select the correct type of fat to eat. You can also determine the right role for fat in your diet.

THE FUNCTIONS OF FAT

Fat actually has a number of vital functions in the body. Fat is needed to absorb the essential vitamins A, D, E and K. These vitamins are called fat-soluble, which means they can only be assimilated in the presence of fat. For example, fats are needed to produce vitamin A from carotene, and are required to absorb vitamin D so it can carry calcium to the teeth and bones. Fat also contains the essential nutrients linoleic and linolenic acid, which, like the essential amino acids, cannot be produced by the body and must be supplied by the diet. Linoleic acid assists in the growth process. Deficiencies in these essential fatty acids can actually stunt the growth of children and lead to dry, rough or flaky skin in adults.

Fatty substances also provide many of the flavors and aromas in food, which add to our eating pleasure. Taking away these ingredients can reduce the satisfaction we get from our diet, even if the number of calories is relatively unchanged. The presence of fat in foods also causes the pyloric valve between the stomach and small intestine to constrict in size. This keeps the food in the stomach longer, giving you the full feeling that is so satisfying after a meal. In fact, the reason that people say they are hungry so quickly after a Chinese meal is because the lowfat content of most Chinese dishes keeps the pyloric valve open, allowing the food to pass out of the stomach and into the small intestine quicker than after your typically fat-laden Italian or French meal. Also, fat in the small intestine stimulates hormones that inhibit hunger contractions in the stomach. These feelings of emptiness or fullness are largely independent of the total number of calories eaten.

Body fat also serves as the body's long-term energy source, providing energy for all tissues of the body except the brain, nerves and lungs. Since the body has only a limited capacity to store carbohydrates and proteins, all nutrients that are not immediately needed for energy or anabolic activities are converted to fats and stored in the adipose tissues for later use. This allows the body to maintain its normal functioning between meals and during prolonged periods of relative starvation.

The fat stores are especially important as an energy source during light and moderate exercise, which is an aerobic activity. During long periods of jogging, for example, up to 80 percent of the energy produced comes from the fat stores. That is why it is so important to include aerobic activities in a program of weight reduction. At the same time, it should be noted that anaerobic sports such as weight-lifting and sprinting do not use fats as an energy source, since these activities are so intense and short-term that the body's aerobic energy system cannot be geared up for action quickly enough to be of assistance. These anaerobic activities are powered by the glycogen and glucose in the working muscles.

Fat also helps insulate the body from cold weather. Most of the body's fat stores are located underneath the skin and are called subcutaneous. These subcutaneous deposits guard against the excessive loss of body heat when climatic temperatures are low, but they increase total body weight and hide the definition of the muscles—much to the frustration of the bodybuilder. Subcutaneous fat also restricts the escape of body heat during exercise. At the same time, fat protects the body's internal organs from injury by providing a cushion of protective material which softens the shocks that can occur during accidents. The liver, kidneys, heart and brain have large amounts of these fat deposits.

Although subcutaneous fat helps the body from feeling cold, wearing the proper clothing can also serve this purpose. These fat stores are therefore called nonessential. The fat surrounding the internal organs is necessary for survival, however, so these fat stores are called essential. The essential body fat level is generally considered to be around 3 percent of total body weight for men and 6 percent for women.

THE THREE KINDS OF FAT

Most naturally occurring fat in the diet is made up of molecules with three fatty-acid chains linked to a glycerol molecule. For this reason, these fat molecules are called triglycerides. The characteristics of each of these three fatty-acid chains determine what the resulting fat will be like.

Fatty-acid chains can fall into one of two main types: saturated and unsaturated. The difference between these two types lies in their chemical composition. All fats are combinations of carbon, oxygen and hydrogen atoms that are linked together in a variety of ways. When these atoms are linked so that pairs of hydrogen atoms are bonded to all the available sites on the carbon atoms, the fatty acid is said to be saturated with hydrogen atoms. These saturated fats, such as butter and lard, are always solid at room temperature. On the other hand, if some of the carbon atoms are not linked to hydrogen atoms at points where they could be attached, the fatty acid is called unsaturated. Oils that are liquid at room temperature, such as corn, safflower and olive oils, are unsaturated.

The category of unsaturated can be further divided into monounsaturated and polyunsaturated, depending on the number of bonding sites that are not filled with hydrogen atoms. Monounsaturated fats, as their name implies, are missing only one pair of hydrogen atoms to be fully saturated. Polyunsaturated fats are even more unsaturated than the monounsaturated fats. Examples of fats that are monounsaturated include avocado, olive and peanut oils. Corn, soybean and safflower oils, on the other hand, are polyunsaturated fats. Polyunsaturated fats are thinner liquids at room temperature than monounsaturated fats.

All sources of fat have a mixture of both saturated and unsaturated fats in them. As a general rule, animal fats are predominately saturated while vegetable oils are mostly unsaturated. There are exceptions, however. Palm kernel and coconut oils are made up of mostly saturated fatty acids, while chicken fat has a great deal of unsaturated fat. Fish oils are also high in polyunsaturated fatty acids.

The importance of these categories is that studies have shown statistical connections between atherosclerosis (hardening of the arteries) and the level of saturated fat in the diet. Saturated fats have been shown to raise the amount of cholesterol in the blood and to increase the risk of atherosclerosis, while unsaturated fats seem to have less effect. As a result, it is best to keep your consumption of saturated fats to a minimum. Moreover, high levels of fat consumption have been connected to diabetes, obesity, hypertension and even cancer. They can adversely effect the transport of glucose into skeletal muscle, restricting the formation of the glycogen stores. They can even reduce the effectiveness of insulin and the oxygen-carrying capacity of the blood. For these reasons, it is also wise for natural athletes to restrict the total amount of fat in their diets.

A word of caution is in order for an artificial crossbreed of oil called hydrogenated, sometimes partially hydrogenated, vegetable oil. This oil, which is a frequent ingredient in many store-bought foods, is actually unsaturated vegetable oil which has been chemically processed to add hydrogen atoms to it. While this chemical manipulation increases the amount of time the product can sit on the shelf and cuts the cost of producing it compared to starting with a hydrogenated fat like butter, it also converts a relatively healthy unsaturated fat into a more saturated and less healthy ingredient. Products which contain hydrogenated vegetable oils should be avoided for the same reasons you steer away from saturated fats. Don't be misled by this trick of the food processors.

DIETARY GUIDELINES

Here are some Dietary Guidelines for fats:

Keep fat consumption to a minimum. While it is necessary to consume some fat to absorb the fat-soluble vitamins and to obtain the essential fatty acids linoleic and linolenic acid, you can get your daily requirement of fat from a diet which contains only 20 grams of fat (around five to six percent of the average athlete's total caloric intake). Needless to say, this is far less than nearly everyone takes in. There is no nutritional reason to eat any more fat than this, although studies have shown that somewhat higher percentages of dietary fat can be tolerated by the body without any negative effects on your health. Still, it is wise to restrict your total fat intake.

The recommended percentage of fat calories in the diet depends on the source you use. The U.S. Government, in an attempt to be realistic with the general population, sets its suggested limit at 30 percent of total calories. Many nutritionists say that a diet which is 20 percent fat will provide even more protection from heart disease and atherosclerosis, while the Pritikin Foundation suggests 10 percent as the most healthy guideline. For natural athletes who are interested in health and maximum athletic performance, the best guideline seems to be a diet of 15 percent fat during the training season, dropping to five percent during the contest preparation period. This will result in a year-round average of about 10 percent, yet still assure maximum glycogen storage during your competition season. In all cases you will be eating enough fat to meet your minimum requirement of fatty acids. Remember, however, that a gram of fat has nine calories—more than twice the caloric content of a gram of protein and carbohydrate—so the calories can add up quickly.

Stay away from saturated fats. Saturated fats have been connected to several cardiovascular diseases, so try to restrict your saturated fat consumption to 20 percent of your total fat calories (1 to 3 percent of total daily calories). While most all fatty products contain a mixture of saturated and unsaturated fats, you can minimize your exposure to saturated fat by eating mostly fish, poultry and egg whites for your protein sources. This will keep your total fat intake down as well. Reduce your beef, pork and egg yolk consumption to a minimum, and when you do eat beef buy a very lean cut and trim away all the visible fat. Throw out your butter dish and keep on driving past those fast food restaurants. (There are many more suggestions in the Diet Tips chapters.) So improve your health and natural athletic performance by restricting your saturated fat and total fat consumption to the percentages shown in these Guidelines. It really can make a difference.

CHAPTER SIX

More On Diet And Nutrition

While eating the right amount of protein, carbohydrate and fat is vital to sound nutrition, there are several other nutrients which natural athletes need to consider. Many of these nutrients have received a great deal of attention recently. Fiber and cholesterol, for example, are the subjects of countless advertisements urging us to buy a particular product for its reputed health benefits. Vitamins and minerals have also been common topics on talk shows and in the press, where the virtues and dangers of supplementation are often discussed. Less talked about, but just as important, is water, which is sometimes not even considered to be a nutrient. Yet optimal sports performance depends on the right quantity of water in the body. Without this vital nutrient we die in a matter of days—far sooner than from any other nutritional deficiency.

The characteristics of each of these nutrients are reviewed in this chapter, and Dietary Guidelines are presented which indicate the amount of each nutrient necessary for sound nutrition. This chapter also looks at a variety of so-called ergogenic aids—supplements which are claimed to improve athletic endurance and performance. The claims of supplement manufacturers are compared to the findings of unbiased scientific research to see which ergogenic aids the natural athlete should consider using. The chapter concludes with a discussion on how you can control your bodyweight.

Fiber and Cholesterol

There has been a great deal of discussion recently about the dangers of cholesterol and the need for fiber in the diet. Studies have connected high blood levels of cholesterol with hardening of the arteries and other cardiovascular diseases. At the same time, studies have shown that certain types of fiber seem to reduce cholesterol levels and help prevent some cancers, although factors like a lowfat diet may also play a role. Not all fibers are alike, however, and, to make it more complex, cholesterol is transported throughout the body in a number of ways. Making the right dietary choices can have a significant impact on your long-term health.

CHOLESTEROL

While most people feel that cholesterol is a useless substance that can only harm their health, the truth is that cholesterol is a necessary component for the human body. Cholesterol is an essential part of every cell. It is utilized by the liver to produce the bile acids which absorb fat in the small intestine, and it is required to synthesize vitamin D. Cholesterol is also a raw material for the production of several hormones, including aldosterone and testosterone. So cholesterol is essential to good health. Eating cholesterol, however, is not. The liver produces all the cholesterol that the body ever needs.

Cholesterol is present in the membranes of fish and all animals, so whenever you eat their meat, eggs, organs or milk you will get some cholesterol along with it. Egg yolks and organs, like heart and liver, have the highest amount of cholesterol, while meat is lower. Most meats and fish, with the exception of shellfish, have about the same amount of cholesterol per ounce (14-18 milligrams). Milk products vary considerably, with the quantity of cholesterol related to the amount of butterfat in the particular product.

High levels of cholesterol in the blood have been associated with hardening of the arteries (atherosclerosis), which is a leading cause of death in most industrialized nations. There is some question, however, as to the impact that dietary cholesterol has on the level of cholesterol in the blood, since the liver also produces great quantities of it. It appears that the role of dietary cholesterol varies with the individual. Some persons seem to be able to eat large amounts of cholesterol without any change in their blood level, while other people respond rapidly to changes in their cholesterol intake. The exact relationship between cholesterol in the diet and in the blood is therefore unclear at this time. What is clear is that dietary cholesterol is not necessary for health, so natural athletes should restrict their cholesterol intake as much as possible.

Cholesterol is transported throughout the body in small carrier vehicles called lipoproteins. These lipoproteins, which contain fats (lipids), proteins and cholesterol, allow the oily fats and cholesterol to be transported through the watery medium of the blood. Without lipoproteins, these oily products would separate from the blood like cream rising in a bottle of non-homogenized milk. Lipoproteins take fats and cholesterol from the intestinal tract to the liver and all other cells of the body.

There are actually four different types of lipoproteins: chylomicrons, VLDL, LDL and HDL. The chylomicrons are responsible for transporting dietary cholesterol to the liver and dietary fats to the fat cells. VLDLs (very low density lipoproteins) carry the fats that are manufactured in the liver (but not dietary fats) to the fat cells for storage. They also contain cholesterol.

LDL (low density lipoproteins) is the name given to the VLDLs after they deposit their fat molecules in the fat cells, which makes them proportionately higher in cholesterol. LDLs contain almost 75 percent of the cholesterol in the bloodstream. It is the LDLs that are responsible for supplying cholesterol to all the cells of the body when they need it. HDLs (high density lipoproteins) act as a counterforce to the LDLs. Their role is to take excess cholesterol from the cells and the bloodstream and return it to the liver for use in digesting fats or elimination from the body.

The HDLs are considered to be good lipoproteins, while the VLDLs and LDLs are bad lipoproteins. This is because the VLDLs and LDLs tend to stick to the walls of the arteries as they transport cholesterol to the cells. HDLs, on the other hand, carry cholesterol away from the arterial walls to the liver. A high ratio of HDLs to LDLs is therefore considered to reduce the risk of heart disease, while a low ratio of HDLs to LDLs increases the chances of atherosclerosis, especially when other risk factors, such as smoking, high blood pressure, obesity or diabetes, are present. As noted earlier, steroid use significantly reduces HDL levels. In fact, some drug users have HDL levels so low that they are undetectable in laboratory tests!

There are several things you can do to improve your HDL/LDL ratio. One of the most important is regular exercise, especially aerobic exercise. You should also reduce the quantity of fat that you eat as well, especially saturated fat. Fat consumption has been connected with high blood levels of LDLs—regardless of the actual cholesterol content of the fatty foods.

There has been a lot of discussion recently about the virtues of fish oil. It appears that the omega-3 fatty acids in some cold water fish, especially salmon and mackerel, can reduce LDL levels in the blood. They also appear to reduce the chances of blood clotting. Don't go out and fill up on salmon, however. The role of omega-3 needs to be kept in perspective. Salmon and mackerel have lots of fat in them, so the omega-3 only mitigates some of the damage that would have been caused by these fats in its absence. So if the choice is between salmon and T-bone steak, by all means eat the salmon. But if the choice is between cod or halibut and salmon, stick with the lower-fat fish as a general rule. Omega-3 is not a miracle cure that allows you to eat all the fat you like. A lowfat diet is still best.

FIBER

Much has been written about the connection between fiber and cholesterol. It appears that a low-fiber diet is correlated with high blood-cholesterol levels and numerous diseases, including hypertension, heart disease, diabetes and colon cancer. A diet which is high in fiber can reduce the incidence of these diseases, while reducing the level of cholesterol in the blood.

Fiber is the component of plant foods which cannot be broken down by the human digestive system. There are actually two kinds of fiber: water-soluble and water-insoluble. Water-soluble fiber is capable of absorbing many times its weight in water, while water-insoluble fibers absorb relatively less. Both types of fiber pass chemically unchanged through the entire intestinal tract, providing bulk and roughage that promotes the proper movement of material to the colon. This reduces the chances of colon cancer.

These fibers also appear to slow down and even out the absorption of glucose into the bloodstream, so the pancreas is not forced to react to major swings in glucose levels by producing large amounts of insulin. This can be of particular benefit to diabetics, who have insulin deficiencies. Both types of fiber also bind with certain potentially cancer-causing agents in foods, helping remove them from the body before they can cause damage.

Soluble fiber is also capable of binding with the bile acids that take cholesterol from the liver to the intestines, which facilitates the removal of cholesterol from the body. This lowers the LDL level in the blood and improves the HDL/LDL ratio. It is felt that soluble fiber may also inhibit the absorption of cholesterol in the first place. Insoluble fiber is unable to bind with these bile acids and therefore has no benefit in reducing cholesterol levels.

Fiber may also help in controlling body weight. Since it takes longer to eat high-fiber foods, the stomach gets its sensation of fullness before a great deal of food has been eaten. Fiber-rich foods stay in the stomach longer as well, prolonging that satisfied feeling after eating. It also takes more energy to digest and assimilate high-fiber foods, so the net caloric contribution to the fat stores is less.

About the only negative effect of fiber is that it reduces the absorption of certain minerals, including calcium, iron and zinc. For this reason, excessive amounts of fiber (over 40 grams a day) should be avoided. Foods that are relatively better sources of soluble fiber include oatmeal and oat bran, carrots, potatoes, corn, apples and citrus fruits, psyllium and legumes like peas, lentils and most beans. Mainly insoluble fiber can be found in brown rice, strawberries, wheat bran and wheat products like spaghetti and bread.

DIETARY GUIDELINES

Here are some Dietary Guidelines for fiber and cholesterol:

Eat foods which are high in fiber. By now, almost everyone accepts that a high-fiber diet is good for you. While some of the supposed health benefits of fiber may in fact be due to a lowfat diet, this is no reason to get blasé about the need for fiber. Try to eat at least 20 grams of fiber per day. Since fiber is contained in fruits, vegetables and many grains (with the notable exception of white rice), increase the amount of these foods in your diet. Cut back on the amounts of processed foods, such as white breads and fruit juices, which have had the fiber taken out of them. Moreover, because soluble fiber has been connected with more health benefits, choose foods which have a high proportion of soluble fiber as often as possible.

Keep your cholesterol consumption to a minimum. Your body produces all the cholesterol it needs in the liver, so there is never any reason to put additional cholesterol into your system. Still, cholesterol is contained in all meats, poultry, fish and dairy products, so cutting it out entirely would put a rather severe crimp in most people's diets. The American Heart Association suggests a daily cholesterol intake of 300 milligrams per day, which is a third less than most people take in. You should try to do even better than this.

Here are several things you can do to minimize your cholesterol intake. Forget about egg yolks. You can eat more than a half-pound of cheese and get less cholesterol than in one single extra-large egg yolk. The proper place for egg yolks is in the garbage disposal. If this idea is too radical for you, at least reduce the number of yolks you eat along with your egg whites. Also, try to reduce the amount of fat, especially saturated fat, that you eat. While the quantity of cholesterol per ounce is about the same for most animal and fish flesh, the quantity of fat that goes along with it varies considerably. Since fat has also been implicated in atherosclerosis and other health problems, it makes sense to eat as little fat as possible along with your cholesterol. Refer to the Dietary Guidelines on fat to get more information.

Vitamins and Minerals

Natural athletes are constantly bombarded with advertisements about the latest "discoveries" on vitamins and minerals. It seems almost every month some supplement manufacturer brings out a new study which "proves" that their particular product can make that major difference in your athletic performance. All you need to do is take some of these special high-potency megasupplements and you will be converted into the superperson you have always dreamed of. It would be wonderful if sports excellence were that easy. Unfortunately, it is not.

VITAMINS

Vitamins are chemical substances which are needed in minute amounts by the body. There are currently 13 of these substances that are recognized as essential for humans: vitamin A (retinol), B1 (thiamine), B2 (riboflavin), B3 (niacin), B6 (pyridoxine), B12 (cobalamin), pantothenic acid, folic acid, biotin, C, D, E and K. Even though the amounts required by the body are small, a deficiency of any one of them can lead to illness and disease.

Vitamins are required for many different chemical reactions within the body. They help regulate the chain of metabolic reactions which controls tissue synthesis and the release of energy in food. Vitamin

B1, for example, plays a significant role in energy production. Without the right vitamins these chemical reactions cannot take place at the proper rates, impacting the body's metabolic processes. Some vitamins also act as antioxidants, protecting the body from potentially cancer-causing chemicals called free radicals.

Vitamin deficiencies, therefore, can have a major impact on athletic performance. Once the deficiency has been eliminated, however, it has not been shown in any controlled, scientific study that athletes get incremental benefits in performance from vitamin supplementation. On the contrary, excessive amounts of vitamins are either excreted in the urine (so you are basically wasting your money) or may actually become toxic to the system, producing many negative side effects.

There are two types of vitamins: fat-soluble and water-soluble. The fat-soluble vitamins (A, D, E and K) can only be dissolved in fat and not in water. A minimal amount of fat must therefore be included in the diet so that these vitamins can be assimilated and used by the body. As was noted earlier, a diet with 20 grams of fat is sufficient to meet these needs. Fat-soluble vitamins that are not immediately needed are stored in the adipose tissues for later use, so deficiencies of this type of vitamins are relatively rare. Yet because these vitamins remain in the system for so long, natural athletes who take high levels of fat-soluble vitamin supplements can actually develop toxic levels of these vitamins in their bodies. For this reason, great care should be taken when using fat-soluble vitamin supplements.

The water-soluble vitamins (B-complex vitamins and vitamin C) act as coenzymes, combining with other small protein molecules to form active enzymes. These vitamins dissolve in water but not in fat. As a result, they cannot be stored to any great degree by the body. Water-soluble vitamin supplies that are not immediately needed are likely to be excreted in the urine. It is therefore necessary to eat foods that contain these vitamins on a regular basis to prevent deficiencies.

On the following pages is a table listing all of the 13 vitamins essential for human health. The Recommended Daily Allowance for each vitamin is provided, along with the foods which contain them and the functions they perform in the body. Since the RDA has been established for sedentary persons, it is sometimes felt that natural athletes have higher vitamin requirements due to their greater energy and metabolic expenditures. However, vitamins have the ability to be used over and over in metabolic reactions, so it is unlikely that the vitamin needs of the athlete are significantly greater than those of the average person. Even if they were, the much greater food consumption of the athlete would assure that enough vitamins were obtained from the diet without the need for major supplementation.

TABLE 3
VITAMINS

VITAMIN	RDA (mg.)*	DIETARY SOURCES	FUNCTIONS
FAT SOLUBLE			
VITAMIN A (Retinol)	1.0 0.8	Dark green and yellow vegetables, milk, eggs, butter	Required for growth, formation of hair and skin, night vision
VITAMIN D	0.075 0.075	Eggs, dairy products, fortified milk, margarine, liver	Increases absorption of calcium, formation of bones and teeth
VITAMIN E (Tocopherol)	10 8	Seeds, green leafy vegetables, grains, shortening and oils	Antioxidant (prevents cell damage), muscle and red blood cell formation
VITAMIN K	0.07-0.14 0.07-0.14	Egg yolks, potatoes, liver, green leafy vegetables	Clotting of blood
WATER SOLUBLE			
VITAMIN B-1 (Thiamine)	1.4-1.5 1.0-1.1	Grains and cereals, peas and beans	Plays role in energy production
VITAMIN B-2 (Riboflavin)	1.6-1.7 1.2-1.3	Grains and cereals, milk, eggs and meat, green vegetables	Helps release energy from foods

* The first RDA value is for men, the second value is for women.

VITAMIN	RDA (mg.)*	DIETARY SOURCES	FUNCTIONS
VITAMIN B-3 (Niacin)	18-19 13-14	Grains, legumes, meats and poultry, eggs, nuts	Plays role in energy production
VITAMIN B-6 (Pyridoxine)	2.2 2.0	Meats and nuts, cereals, green leafy vegetables	Breaks down protein and glycogen, builds blood components
VITAMIN B-12	0.003 0.003	Milk, eggs, meat, liver and kidneys	Nervous system, helps form red blood cells
PANTO-THENIC ACID	4-7 4-7	Found in nearly all foods	Plays role in energy production
FOLIC ACID	0.4 0.4	Dark green leafy vegetables, liver, wheat, legumes	Helps form amino acids, hemoglobin in blood
BIOTIN	0.1-0.2 0.1-0.2	Egg yolks, legumes, dark leafy green vegetables	Helps form amino and fatty acids, glycogen
VITAMIN C (Ascorbic Acid)	60 60	Citrus fruits, tomatoes, green peppers, green leafy vegetables	Helps strengthen immune system; bone, teeth and collagen formation

The first RDA value is for men, the second value is for women.

MINERALS

Minerals are also essential for good health. Minerals are found in the body's enzymes and hormones, as well as in the structural elements of the body. While vitamins are able to facilitate chemical reactions in the body without actually becoming part of them, minerals usually become incorporated within the body's physical and chemical structures. They play an essential role in formation of the teeth and bones, and are involved in functions as diverse as maintaining a normal heart beat and regulating the acid-base balance of the body.

Minerals allow the muscles to contract and permit the nerves to transmit impulses. They also regulate cellular metabolism and stimulate various reactions that allow energy to be released from the foods we eat.

There are 22 minerals which are currently recognized as essential to human health: calcium, phosphorus, sulfur, potassium, chlorine, sodium, magnesium, iron, fluorine, zinc, copper, selenium, iodine, chromium, cobalt, silicon, vanadium, tin, nickel, manganese, molybdenum and lead. These minerals are found naturally in water and the foods we eat, so getting enough minerals is usually not a problem nowadays. In the last century, persons far from the sea (like in the Midwestern United States) frequently had iodine deficiencies because they ate so little salt-water fish. The introduction of iodized salt solved this problem, however.

Minerals have been divided into two groups—major minerals and trace minerals—depending on the quantities of the mineral that are required for health. There are no chemical differences between these two groups. Individual minerals do vary, however, in the degree to which they are absorbed by the body. This variation, called bioavailability, can range from as low as 5 percent absorption for manganese to 30-40 percent for calcium and magnesium. The bioavailability of a mineral is taken into consideration when the Recommended Daily Allowance for that mineral is established.

It should be noted that the levels of toxicity for minerals are much lower than they are for vitamins. After all, minerals are metals, and metals should be treated with a great deal of respect. There is a lot of public awareness about the dangers of lead poisoning, which can lead to some major physical disabilities. Yet sometimes the same people who wouldn't think of eating lead will willingly take the latest chromium-based fad product, figuring that since it's in a pill it can't be bad for you. Wrong! It is very easy to get toxic levels of minerals. You should never take more than 10 times the RDA of a mineral under any circumstances. In fact, since controlled, scientific studies indicate that there are no benefits to taking minerals beyond the Recommended Daily Allowance, you should only be concerned about getting that level.

In the chart on the next several pages the Recommended Daily Allowance for the essential minerals is listed (if established), along with the functions each mineral has in the body and the foods which contain it. This should provide you with some guidelines for your diet program.

TABLE 4
MINERALS

MINERAL	RDA (mg.)*	DIETARY SOURCES	FUNCTIONS
MAJOR MINERALS			
CALCIUM	800 800	Milk, cheese, legumes, dark green vegetables	Builds bones, teeth and nerves; muscle contraction; blood clotting
PHOSPHORUS	800 800	Milk, cheese, grains, meats, poultry, fish, soft drinks	Builds bones and teeth; component of ATP (energy currency)
SULFUR	Not yet established	Protein-rich foods	Needed to form connective tissue, tendons, cartilage
POTASSIUM	1875-5100 1700-5100	Grains, meats, most fruits, nuts, legumes	Electrolyte (keeps acid-base balance); nerve conduction; muscle contraction
CHLORINE	1700-5100 1700-5100	Table salt and salt substitute; "fast" and prepared foods	Electrolyte (keeps acid-base balance); ingredient in stomach acid
SODIUM	1100-3300	Table salt; "fast" and prepared foods	Electrolyte (keeps acid-base balance); needed for nerve functioning

The first RDA value is for men, the second value is for women.

MINERAL	RDA (mg.)*	DIETARY SOURCES	FUNCTIONS
MAGNESIUM	350 300	Green leafy vegetables, grains, soybeans, nuts	Needed for healthy bones; helps release energy from food; aids nerve impulses

TRACE MINERALS

MINERAL	RDA (mg.)*	DIETARY SOURCES	FUNCTIONS
IRON	10 18	Meats, eggs, grains, legumes, leafy vegetables	Forms hemoglobin and myoglobin in blood; helps release energy
FLUORINE	1.5-4.0 1.5-4.0	Drinking water, seafood, teas	Helps prevent cavities; builds stronger bones, teeth
ZINC	15 15	Beef, oyster, dark poultry meat, some nuts and whole grains	Regulates food metabolism through enzyme activity
COPPER	2-3 2-3	Potatoes, nuts, organ meats, shellfish	Aids fat metabolism, energy production; helps form red blood cells
SELENIUM	0.05-0.2 0.05-0.2	Some vegetables, grains; meat and seafood	Antioxidant (protects cell membrane from damage)
IODINE	0.15	Fish from sea, eggs, iodized salt, meat, dairy products	Used by thyroid to regulate metabolism; protein synthesis
CHROMIUM	0.05-0.2 0.05-0.2	Yeast, apple skins, oysters, fats, meats	Works with insulin to control metabolism

The first RDA value is for men, the second value is for women.

MINERAL	RDA (mg.)*	DIETARY SOURCES	FUNCTIONS
COBALT	Is part of Vitamin B-12	Vegetables, grains	Needed for Vitamin B-12 to function
SILICON	Not yet established	Water	Helps form skin and connective tissues; may help prevent heart disease
VANADIUM	Not yet established	Still unknown	May regulate fat metabolism
TIN	Not yet established	Canned foods	May increase growth
NICKEL	Not yet established	Vegetables	May increase energy production
MANGANESE	Not yet established	Fruits and green vegetables, grains and nuts	May play role in fat synthesis and energy production
MOLYB-DENUM	Not yet established	Grains and legumes, organ meats	Component of several enzymes
LEAD	Not yet established	Canned foods, bone meal	Prevents anemia in small amounts

The first RDA value is for men, the second value is for women.

DIETARY GUIDELINE

Consider whether you need to take a multi-vitamin and multi-mineral supplement. Even though all controlled scientific studies have shown that vitamin and mineral supplementation beyond the RDA does not improve athletic performance, many natural athletes and the general public continue to take these supplements. The usual reason is that it provides a nutritional insurance policy, so the athlete does not need to be overly concerned about getting enough of these nutrients. There is certainly some logic to this, since there are plenty of things in life to worry about besides getting enough leafy, green vegetables. If you like the idea of a nutritional insurance policy, then a multi-vitamin and multi-mineral supplement is recommended.

Note that the suggestion is for *multi*-vitamins and *multi*-minerals. These combination tablets provide moderate dosages of all the necessary vitamins and minerals without providing such excessive megadoses that you wind up pouring your money down the drain or getting toxic reactions. Should you have some temporary deficiency due to the particular foods you ate, the multiple-supplement tablets will take care of it. (The rest of the water-soluble vitamins, of course, just wind up in your urine.) This is more than adequate protection from vitamin and mineral deficiencies.

Sometimes bodybuilders and wrestlers go on restricted-calorie diets to "make weight" for their competitions. During these diet periods their food intake goes down while their energy expenditure goes up. This may result in a modest vitamin or mineral deficiency, depending on the foods consumed. The best course of action is to eat plenty of fresh vegetables and fruits, which are low in calories yet full of vitamins and minerals. Eating proportionately more of these types of foods should eliminate any deficiency which might occur. Still, many athletes would rather insure that they get enough micronutrients by taking supplements. In this situation a multi-vitamin and multi-mineral supplement is more than enough protection.

Stay away from supplements of the individual vitamins and minerals, which provide many times the RDA for a particular nutrient. There is no evidence that such megadoses provide any benefit to the natural athlete. Some people have cabinets full of individual vitamins and minerals. These persons may spend five minutes a day opening and closing bottles and sloshing down pills in the belief that they are improving their sports performance. If only this were true! In effect, these people are just wasting their money. They would be better off investing that hard-earned cash on peptide-bond amino acid supplements and on better quality foods, or saving it for travel expenses to the regional championship!

Even more expensive are the packets of vitamins and minerals that come assembled and ready to swallow. These packets save you the time required to open and close bottles, but you wind up paying through the nose for this convenience without getting any additional benefit over the lower levels obtained in the multi-vitamin and multi-mineral supplements. So don't waste your money. There are plenty of other things to spend it on.

Water

Water is a critical nutrient for the athlete. While you can live with deficiencies of most nutrients for weeks or even months, a few days without water will kill you. Water is vital to even the most sedentary person, since it has many essential roles in the body. For the natural athlete, proper hydration is an absolute requirement for peak performance and strength. This is especially true for the endurance athlete.

There is more water in the body than any other nutrient. Up to 60 percent of a person's body weight is water. It makes up 65 to 75 percent of the weight of muscle, yet only 25 percent of the weight of fat. About two-thirds of this water is located inside the cell, while the other third is extracellular (outside of the cell).

Water is involved in many of the body's functions. It plays a role in digestion, assimilation, circulation and excretion. Water is the major ingredient in blood plasma, which transports nutrients and gases between the cells. It is a necessary part of many chemical reactions in the body. Water also carries off the waste products of energy metabolism from the cell, especially lactic acid, and provides the fluid needed to get rid of the body's wastes. These wastes include the urea that is produced during the breakdown of dietary protein. Water lubricates the joints as well and gives form to the muscles.

A significant amount of water is produced by the body when food molecules are broken down for energy. In fact, nearly 25 percent of the total daily water requirement for a sedentary person can be provided by this metabolic mechanism. Carbohydrate produces the least amount of water, while fat actually creates more weight in water than the weight the fat had to begin with (107 grams of water for each 100 grams of fat)! Each gram of glucose combines with 2.7 grams of water to form glycogen in the muscles and liver. This water is released when the glycogen is converted into energy.

One of the most important functions of water is heat regulation. Exercise generates heat, which can severely impact the functioning of the body if the temperature rises too high. When water is released through the skin and sweat glands and this water evaporates, heat is dissipated into the environment, lowering the skin temperature. This natural air-conditioning system allows exercise to continue.

The heat regulation function can use up a great deal of water, depending on the intensity and duration of exercise and the environmental conditions of relative humidity and air temperature. While a limited amount of water can be lost without affecting sports performance (up to 2 percent of body weight), a loss of only 3 percent can reduce endurance. Even greater losses can impact muscular strength. When the water loss exceeds 6 percent, life-threatening symptoms such as heat exhaustion and heat stroke can occur.

Dehydration causes the blood volume to go down, forcing the heart to work harder. It also interferes with numerous body functions and reduces the amount of water available for use as sweat. Dehydration can actually be speeded up by high-protein diets, since water is diverted to the kidneys to get rid of the excess urea produced by these diets. The way to avoid dehydration is to keep protein intake moderate and to consume water at regular intervals throughout your training sessions. This is especially important in hot weather and during endurance activities like long-distance marathons.

Many foods, including nearly all fruits and most vegetables, contain a great deal of water. Vegetables like lettuce, green beans and broccoli have a very high water content, while meats and other fatty foods contain much less. Grains have little moisture on their own, but can absorb large quantities of water during cooking. Rice, for example, quadruples in size as it cooks. Of course, the greater the water content of a food, the lower its caloric value per portion.

DIETARY GUIDELINE

Make sure you get enough water every day, especially during training sessions. Water is essential to athletic performance. To ensure that you get enough water, eat plenty of foods which are high in water content, and drink 1 1/2 to two liters of water each day (about six to eight glasses). While training, have a few sips of water every once in a while throughout the workout, even if you're not thirsty. Thirst is not a very sensitive indicator of water need. This water should ideally be good quality unflavored water.

Try not to drink excess water with your meals, however. While some water is, of course, needed to swallow your food, too much water can pointlessly dilute the digestive "juices" in your stomach, retarding the digestive process. It's better to drink most of your water between meals if possible.

Avoid sugary sodas and other sucrose-based drinks, including those fruit-juice-based products that boast they are 10 percent real juice. This means they are actually 90 percent unreal, mostly sugar and flavorings. Some sports drinks are made from glucose and fructose, which is better, but the calories you get from them can just as easily be obtained from solid food, and the electrolytes in them are not even needed unless you are in a marathon race more than four hours long.

Natural fruit juices are much better, although they are such concentrated sources of calories they should only make up a small portion of the diet, especially when you are on a reduced-calorie diet to lower your weight for a competition. In these situations your body would rather feel the sensation of fullness that comes from solid food. You're better off eating the fruit, with all its fiber and greater nutrient value, than the juice made from it. In fact, the best thing of all to drink is plain ole water. This is what your body needs, so why not give it what it wants?

Ergogenic Aids

The science of nutrition is relatively new. Each year discoveries are being made, while old and established facts are found to be myths. Sometimes there are even conflicting studies on the same nutrient, such as occurred recently with oat bran. Some studies say that oat bran is one of the greatest health aids ever discovered, while other studies claim that different factors (such as the low-fat content of a diet high in fiber) are responsible for the benefits attributed to it. In this confusing environment it is sometimes hard for the natural athlete to tell right from wrong.

This situation is not made any easier by the overblown claims of some supplement company salespeople. You have no doubt seen advertisements for products that have supposedly been proven effective in "scientific" studies. Yet upon closer examination these studies didn't use control groups or other required methodologies to eliminate bias. Even if they had, the results might not have relevance for a particular sport or even for athletic training in general.

Nowhere does confusion reign more than in the area of ergogenic aids. Ergogenic aids are products which supposedly enhance your ability to perform physical work. There is a long list of products that supplement companies have advanced as ergogenic aids: inosine, gamma oryzanol, succinates, octacosanol, plant sterols, bee pollen, individual amino acid "growth enhancers" like arginine and ornithine, smilax, glandular extracts and many more. There are also "metabolic optimizers" on the market which combine nutrients such as carbohydrates, amino acids, vitamins and minerals with some of these ergogenic aids. From all the advertising claims in the magazines you would think that athletic success was guaranteed if only you took enough of these "magic potions." And it certainly would be nice if this were true (as long as you had the money to buy the products)! Unfortunately, it is not.

Many people are looking for that special pill that will make the crucial difference in their sports performance. Steroid users are well-known for this mentality. Many seem willing to swallow anything and everything they can get their hands on if told it has the potential to improve their physiques. Perhaps this is a logical consequence of our society's obsession with pills and drugs. Well, sorry to disappoint you, but there isn't a magic pill out there. If there were, word would have gotten around by now and everyone would be using it. This is a sad but real fact of life. There are no short cuts to achieving the body of a natural champion. It takes hard work and sound nutrition—not some esoteric pill in a bottle.

In fact, unbiased research has come up with only four products that have any ergogenic benefit at all, and three of these products aren't even considered to be ergogenic aids by most people. Optimal performance can only be achieved when the natural athlete takes in adequate amounts of carbohydrate and protein (amino acids). Therefore, in the strictest sense, carbohydrates and amino acids are ergogenic aids.

The caffeine in coffee and tea can also increase alertness and performance in endurance events. It does this by increasing the use of fatty acids for energy production, which spares the body's glycogen stores. Caffeine also has psychological benefits, which can increase your intensity level during exercise. While these effects are modest, they are significant enough to make caffeine a banned substance at the Olympics. Caffeine can make many people jittery, however, and can cause dehydration due to its stimulation of urine production. Regular consumption of caffeine also minimizes its effects on sports performance, so you should use it sparingly if at all.

The last substance with ergogenic benefit is bicarbonates, also called buffers. Bicarbonates, being alkaline substances, counteract the buildup of lactic acid in the muscle fiber, which temporily postpones the onset of muscle fatigue. While this can be of benefit in a marathon or other speed-related event, it has not been proven that bicarbonates enhance an athlete's strength or muscle mass. As a result, their value for powerlifters, wrestlers or bodybuilders has yet to be demonstrated. Bicarbonates can also cause a severe case of diarrhea, so be careful when experimenting with them!

While most so-called ergogenic aids certainly won't hurt you (unless you take them in megadosages), they aren't likely to improve your performance either, beyond what you could have achieved from a healthy, balanced diet alone. And some products, particularly the metal-based ones such as chromium and boron, can actually be toxic to the body in relatively small amounts. So it pays to be cautious and skeptical when it comes to ergogenic aids. The plain truth is that eating right is the best way to provide your body with the nutrients it needs for peak performance.

Supplement manufacturers often claim that their ergogenic aid produces increased endurance or energy production. These claims are based on their product's supposed ability to trick the body into producing more of a particular enzyme or chemical than it normally produces. Yet even if more chemical were produced (not always the case), the only way that this additional supply of chemical could make any difference in performance would be if it alone were the limiting factor. This is almost never the situation.

Some of the supplement manufacturers also resort to half-truths or outright deception when it comes to product claims. Take the case of plant sterols. There has never been a controlled scientific study indicating that plant sterols have any anabolic effect on humans whatsoever. Nonetheless, some manufacturers push these products because of their attractive name. After all, sterol sure sounds like steroid, so they must be similar or related in some way, right? And since steroids have anabolic properties, surely the sterols must too, right? Wrong. Sterol refers to the particular chemical structure of a group of compounds. It has nothing to do with anabolic characteristics. In fact, one of the sterols, cholesterol, is downright unhealthy for you in large amounts. So don't be fooled by these misleading advertising claims. Their goal is to separate you from your money.

Perhaps you know people in your gym who swear by a particular ergogenic aid. They "know for a fact" that it has made the crucial difference in their sports performance. How can they be wrong? The main reason is that most ergogenic aids "work" because of the placebo effect. If your mind thinks that a product is effective, it can actually stimulate positive physical changes in your body. There are many documented cases of athletes lifting more weight or running faster after being given an ergogenic aid that later turned out to be a sugar pill. The mind is a powerful tool. It is the mind that actually sets the limits of natural athletic performance. The best way to maximize your sports potential, therefore, is to stimulate your mind to its greatest ability. This is discussed more in the chapter entitled **The Eight Training Principles**.

When you hear people at the gym making claims about the effectiveness of an ergogenic aid, you need to think about cause and effect. For example, if someone worked out extra hard, took ornithine before bedtime and then told you they had gotten more growth hormone release, what factor was actually responsible for the greater release of hGH? Some people would say the workout, while the supplement company would surely say the ornithine. (By the way, how is someone going to measure their growth hormone release anyway?)

Since research is constantly taking place in this field, it is possible that some day researchers will actually find an ergogenic aid that works. Yet if someone claims that this has happened, you should approach the new finding with skepticism. Critically analyze all of the claims and counterclaims made for a product. Look at the research studies that were done to determine if they had the proper methodology, like having a control group and placebos. (You could even write the supplement company and ask for a copy of their research!) Then follow your best instinct.

The best advise of all is to forget about ergogenic aids. Our bodies are incredibly complex machines, with thousands of interrelated reactions and control loops. To think that swallowing some plant sterol or ground up gland is going to improve your performance is optimistic at best. Even if an ergogenic aid does have some effect on your body, it is unlikely to produce the changes in athletic ability you are looking for. So put your money into a high-quality diet and your time and mental energy into high-intensity training. That will bring you a far better return on your investment.

Controlling Your Body Weight

The control of body weight, especially body fat, is highly prized in most sports. There is nothing to be gained and much to be lost from excessive amounts of fat on the body. Even natural athletes that must have high bodyweights to compete, such as football linemen and heavyweight wrestlers, need to be concerned with their body-fat levels. Body fat slows down the athlete by increasing the amount of non-productive weight he or she must carry during the performance of a sports movement. In bodybuilding, body fat also hides the muscularity of the athlete, placing the athlete at great competitive disadvantage. The way to achieve a low level of body fat for a competition with the smallest possible loss in lean muscle tissue is by maintaining a diet program that is reasonably controlled all year round.

You have no doubt seen athletes who gain large amounts of weight in the off-season, only to go on crash diets and lose most of it for a competition. It was once felt that this bulk/cut system permitted greater amounts of muscle growth compared to a relatively strict year-round diet program. Bodybuilders on steroids were notorious for bulking and cutting. In the off-season they would fill up on most everything that passed in front of their faces, figuring that this way they were assuring themselves the greatest possible benefit from the drugs they were taking. Of course, when they dieted for a competition they would then take even more drugs to maintain as much muscle as possible while they drastically reduced their food intake to make up for the excess of their previous overeating.

As it turns out, this bulk/cut system is not the best muscle-building program, even for an athlete on drugs. It is definitely not recommended for the natural athlete. The best way to achieve your sport goals is to keep to a diet program that provides you with the nutrients you need—but only in the amounts that you need them—throughout the entire year. Excess consumption of calories in the off-season is not only pointless but actually counterproductive.

Studies have shown that weight-loss programs always result in a loss of some muscle tissue along with the fat, especially when exercise is not included as part of the diet program. As a result, any time that you try to drop those pounds or kilograms for a competition, you will inevitably lose muscle. The best way to minimize this loss in muscle weight and muscle mass is to never gain excess fat in the first place. And the way to do that, of course, is by controlling your food consumption so you never take in more calories than your body needs.

There is no question that this requires discipline. Nobody said athletic excellence would be easy. Yet by following a few simple rules you should be able to achieve your dietary objectives without a great deal of hassle.

DIETARY GUIDELINES

Here are some Guidelines for controlling your bodyweight:

Count your calories all year. This may sound like a radical concept, but it really isn't once you think about it. It makes a lot of sense theoretically, and since it only takes a few minutes a day to do the arithmetic, why don't you give it a try?

Counting calories is not the same as restricting your caloric intake. It is nothing more than a means to an end. The actual number of calories you eat each day will depend on what your end is, that is, on the short-term and long-term goals you have set for your sport activity. During the off-season, your goals will likely be to keep your energy and strength levels high while keeping your body fat under control. You will also be trying to increase your lean body mass, so you'll have added muscle to power your sport efforts. These goals are achieved by maintaining a calorie count that is relatively high.

In this situation you will want to be sure you take in enough calories to support your high-intensity training. In fact, not eating enough food under these circumstances will actually hinder progress toward your goals. So counting calories during the off-season does not mean restricting them in the traditional sense of dieting. It means watching your food composition to make sure you get all of the nutrients you need, while regulating your total intake to make sure you get all the calories your body requires without major disruptive swings in your daily food consumption.

During the pre-competition period, when bodybuilders (and other athletes with weight limits to contend with) restrict their food intake, counting calories is the best way to control the dieting process. Many natural athletes go overboard during this period, figuring that the more they cut back on their calories the better. This winds up being counterproductive, however, because the body responds to this relative deprivation by reducing the basal metabolic rate—the minimum number of calories needed to sustain the body's basic functions—and by increasing the efficiency at which food is processed. This makes it even harder to lose fat, since fewer calories are needed to keep the body going.

The best way to prepare for a competition is to count your calories every day. That way you'll know exactly how much food you're taking in, so you can make precise adjustments in your caloric intake to account for variations in exercise levels. Counting calories also allows you to devise and follow a long-term diet program—one which can be repeated over and over again if you're satisfied with its results (or which can be modified with precision so you'll get better results the next time).

Natural athletes who go through a carbohydrate depletion/loading program to create the maximum possible glycogen stores in their muscles need to count calories to make sure they adequately deplete these stores and later to provide the muscles with all the carbohydrates they need during the loading phase. Guessing and estimating on these critical issues can spell the difference between victory and defeat in many competitions.

Some people try to diet for a competition by using the mirror approach. These people say they don't need to count calories because they get all the information they need from a close look in the mirror. If they aren't losing fat quickly enough, they just reduce the amount of food they eat. The problem with this approach is that they don't have any guidelines for making the necessary changes in their diet. How much do you reduce the amount you eat? If you decide to cut out a baked potato, that may or may not be enough. It's hard to say.

On the other hand, by reducing your food intake by 200 calories (whether it's giving up the baked potato or something else) you have a constant numerical guidepost that adds precision to your diet plan. After all, potatoes vary in size and caloric value. The mirror is a tool to help you determine what your body-fat level is, but nothing more. There are also several electronic fat measurement instruments on the market today that are helpful and a lot more precise than the mirror. None of these tools is a substitute for counting calories.

Counting calories can also make your competition diet a lot more interesting. Sometimes natural athletes will eat the exact same thing every day for weeks on end, since they know from experience (or because someone has told them) that a particular diet "works." And it very well may work. The point is that eating the same thing day in and day out has to get boring. What has probably happened is that the person who made up the diet the athlete is following figured out the calorie count at one time and decided it was appropriate. Our athlete is therefore counting calories in an indirect sort of way. It would be just as effective and a lot more exciting to add variety to the diet by substituting foods of equal caloric value instead of constantly eating the same thing. And the only way you can do that is by counting calories every day.

Counting calories is therefore the most effective system for controlling your bodyweight. Counting your calories in the off-season will ensure that you make the greatest gains toward your sport goals without pointless fat buildup. Counting them during the competition season will ensure steady and accurate progress toward the fat reduction goals you have set without a needless loss in lean muscle. So what if it takes five minutes a day to figure out the calories in the food you eat? (That's really all it takes once you get the hang of it.) Think of all the time you spend at your workouts every week. We're only talking about five minutes a day here! When you think about it, that's a small investment to make to ensure that you get all you possibly can from your hard-core training.

In order to help you in controlling your bodyweight, a two-page calorie chart has been included at the end of this chapter. This chart indicates the number of calories contained in the portions of food that natural athletes are likely to eat, rounded off to the nearest 25 calories. This level of detail is sufficient for most athletes' purposes, and it greatly simplifies the task of counting calories. You will also notice that two copies of the chart have been included. Cut one out and keep it in your wallet or purse so you can count calories at restaurants. Keep the other as a reference in your home. You'll no doubt find that counting calories is a lot easier than you thought.

Treat yourself to a splurge a day. Counting calories does not mean you have to lead a life of puritanical virtue, eating food that only a rabbit could love. While you should always follow the Dietary Guidelines, there is enough flexibility in the Guidelines to allow you to have a splurge a day without breaking the rules and getting overwhelming feelings of guilt. Everyone has his or her own idea of a splurge, and these ideas can vary over time. The important thing to remember is that a splurge per day is fine as long as you limit the quantity of food involved.

If you are going out with friends and they order pizza, you can have a slice or two. Just count the calories in what you eat and add it to your total for the day. If the pizza pushes you over the top of your calorie count for that day, take the excess calories off tomorrow's total. Better yet, if you know you are going out for pizza later, save some room in your calorie count for the splurge. The same reasoning goes for the fat and saturated fat guidelines. Unless you are dieting for a competition, chances are that you will find a modest splurge to be well within your diet parameters for the day. Let reason be your guide. It will make your diet a lot more interesting, and will ensure that you stick to it over the long term.

Always include aerobic exercise in your program to control body weight. Studies have shown that when natural athletes combined dieting with aerobic exercise they lost less muscle tissue than when they tried to lose all their weight through dieting alone. As a result, you should always include aerobic exercise in your diet program. For weight reduction purposes, 30 to 45 minutes of aerobic activity per day is all you need to get results. The increased energy expenditure required by this activity, combined with a modest caloric reduction of 10 percent, trims off excess body fat while keeping your muscles full and ready for action.

Since aerobics enhance your cardiovascular fitness and help raise your basal metabolic rate, it is also a good idea to incorporate some aerobics into your training year-round. This may run counter to what you have heard in the gym. It has been shown in scientific studies that a moderate amount of aerobics (1 to 1 1/2 hours per week) has no negative effect on your strength or muscle development. Greater amounts of aerobics can impact strength, however, so keep track of the quantity of aerobics you do. The time you devote to aerobic activity will depend on your sport and training goals.

When trying to lose fat, alternate periods of high-calorie days and low-calorie days so that your metabolism does not slow down as much. The body is an incredible machine. When faced with a situation that it interprets as famine, it conserves needed energy by lowering the basal metabolic rate and increasing the efficiency at which food is utilized by the body. It also tries to hold on to the fat stores, sensing that they may be needed in the future for critical energy reserves if the famine continues. These evolutionary safeguards have no doubt gotten us to where we are today, instead of at some dead end on the tree of evolution. Yet these body reactions can play havoc with the diet plans of natural athletes if they are not recognized and worked into the diet program.

Earlier it was noted that the most effective diet program includes a modest (10 percent) reduction in calories tied to an increase in aerobic activity. Yet in order to insure that the body does not interpret this caloric reduction as the start of a famine condition, it is necessary to "fool" it by alternating periods of high- and low-calorie days in the diet. That way it is hard for the body to decide what is going on, and the metabolic rate will decline at a slower rate.

For example, if you are currently eating 3,000 calories per day, you would begin your fat-reducing diet by setting your average daily calorie level at 2,700. Instead of eating 2,700 calories every day, however, you would alternate two-day periods of 2,900 and 2,500 calories (200 calories above and below your weekly average). For example, you would eat 2,900 calories on Monday and Tuesday, 2,500 on Wednesday and Thursday, etc. This gives your body something close to the calorie level it was used to half the time and should put a brake on the slowing down of your metabolism. The higher your metabolic rate, of course, the more fat you will burn at a given caloric intake, so make it a point to include this daily roller coaster in your diet. It really can make a difference.

The guidelines indicated above are geared toward the average athlete, and will produce very good results for that person. Still, everyone is different. If you lose more than two pounds of body weight per week, you are dieting too severely. Increase your caloric intake, reduce your aerobics somewhat or both. On the other hand, if your metabolism is on the slow side you may find that a somewhat greater caloric reduction is needed to reach your final weight goal. Take your time, though, and don't rush it. Stay with the guidelines noted above until they no longer produce additional results. If you lose two pounds the first week, you may very well lose an additional two pounds the second week with the exact same calorie count.

As in many things, patience is a virtue in dieting. Don't expect results overnight, because if you try to get them that quickly you will knock your metabolism out of kilter and wind up retaining fat. Look at bodyweight control as a long-term venture. Most people who lose weight rapidly put it back on just as swiftly, and often they have proportionally more fat and less muscle fiber than they had to begin with. Slow and steady wins the race. Let that principle be your guide, and you will never again have a problem in controlling your body weight.

TABLE 5
CALORIE CHART

BREADS

All breads, not buttery	1 ounce	75
Bagel	1 large	225
Muffin, English	1 regular	150
Muffin, sweet or corn	1 medium	200
Roll, buttery	1 medium	175
Roll, reg. whole wheat	1 medium	125
Slice of bread	1 regular	75
Slice of bread	1 large	100

DAIRY PRODUCTS

Cheese		
All regular varieties	1 ounce	100
Shredded regular	1/2 cup	175
Modified lowfat	1 ounce	75
Shredded modified	1/2 cup	125
Cottage Cheese	1 cup	200
Eggs	6 jumbo whites	125
Eggs	3 whole ex. large	300
Ice cream, regular	1 cup	275
Ice cream, "gourmet"	1 cup	300
Milk, lowfat	1 cup	150
Milk, skim	1 cup	100
Sherbet	1 cup	250
Yogurt		
Frozen lowfat	1 cup	175
Frozen nonfat	1 cup	75
Nonfat, flavored	1 cup	200
Plain nonfat	1 cup	150

FATS AND OILS

Butter	1 tablespoon	100
Margarine	1 tablespoon	100
Mayonnaise	1 tablespoon	100
Pan coating, no-stick	1 sec. spray	0
Vegetable oils	1 tablespoon	125

FISH AND SEAFOOD*

Catfish	8 ounces	225
Cod	8 ounces	175
Crab	8 ounces	200
Flounder	8 ounces	175
Haddock	8 ounces	175
Halibut	8 ounces	225
Lobster	8 ounces	200
Mahi-Mahi	8 ounces	225
Perch	8 ounces	225
Salmon	8 ounces	400
Scallops	8 ounces	175
Seabass, northern	8 ounces	225
Shrimp, shelled	8 ounces	200
Snapper	8 ounces	200
Sole	8 ounces	175
Swordfish	8 ounces	275
Trout, rainbow	8 ounces	375
Tuna, fresh	8 ounces	250
Tuna, canned	6.5 ounces	225
Whitefish (roughy)	8 ounces	350

FRUIT, FRESH AND DRIED

Apple	1 medium	100
Applesauce	1 cup	125
Apricot, dried	1/2 cup	150
Apricot, fresh	3 medium	100
Avocado	1/2 medium	175
Banana	1 large	125
Cantaloupe	1/2 medium	75
Casaba melon	1 cup chunks	25
Cherry	1 cup	75
Grapes	1 cup	100
Honeydew	1 cup chunks	50
Kiwi	1 medium	50
Mango	1 medium	150
Olive, ripe	3 large	50
Orange, navel	1 large	75
Papaya	1/2 large	75
Peach	1 medium	50
Pear	1 medium	125
Pineapple	1 cup (3/4 inch slice)	75
Plantain	1 large, cooked	150
Plum	3 medium	100
Prune	1/4 cup	100
Raisin	1/4 cup	125
Raspberry, red	1 cup	75
Strawberry	1/2 pint	50
Tangerine	1 large	50
Watermelon	2 cups chunks	50

FRUIT JUICE

Apple	1 cup	125
Cranberry	1 cup	150
Grape	1 cup	150
Grapefruit	1 cup	100
Lemonade	1 cup	125
Orange	1 cup	125
Pineapple	1 cup	150
Sparklers with juice	10 ounces	125

MEATS AND POULTRY*

Beef		
Flank steak	8 ounces	325
Ground beef (8% fat)	8 ounces	400
Ground beef (15% fat)	8 ounces	525
Round steak	8 ounces	425
Sirloin steak	8 ounces	475

* All values are for uncooked lean cuts and filets, with skin and visible fat removed.

TABLE 5
CALORIE CHART

Chicken		
Breast, boneless	8 ounces	375
Breast, with bone	8 ounces	225
Thigh, with bone	8 ounces	275
Lamb, extra lean	8 ounces	425
Turkey		
Breast, boneless	8 ounces	350
Ground (10% fat)	8 ounces	400
Veal, cutlet	8 ounces	425

MISCELLANEOUS

Cereals		
Corn Flakes	1 cup	75
Grape Nuts	1/2 cup	275
Hot cereals	1 ounce dry	100
Oat bran	1/2 cup dry	175
Oatmeal	1/2 cup dry	150
Raisin Bran	1 cup	150
Shredded Wheat	2 large biscuits	150
Wheatena	1/2 cup dry	275
Crackers		
Rice cakes & crackers	each	25
Soda, saltine	2 squares	25
Tortilla chips	1 ounce (1 cup)	150
Lasagna	4" x 4"	450
Nuts		
Coconut	1/4 cup	75
Most raw nuts	1/4 cup	200
Most roasted nuts	1/4 cup	225
Peanut butter	1 tablespoon	75
Pistachio	25 in shell	100
Pancakes	1 6-inch diameter	150
Pizza, cheese/mushroom		
	1/8 of 12-inch pie	250
Popcorn		
Air-popped	1 cup	25
Theatre—no butter	1 cup	50
Salad dressing		
Fat-free	1 tablespoon	0
Reduced calorie	1 tablespoon	50
Regular	1 tablespoon	75
Soup		
Consomme, broth	1 cup	25
Cream-based, chowder	1 cup	125
Noodle with broth	1 cup	75
Spaghetti sauce		
Nonfat	1/2 cup	50
Regular	1/2 cup	100
Spices	all types	0

Tortilla, corn	3 average	200
Tortilla, flour	1 medium	125

RICE AND PASTA

All pastas, noodles	4 ounces dry	400
All pastas, noodles	1 cup cooked	200
Noodles	1 cup uncooked	175
Pasta shells	1 cup unckd.	250
Rice, brown or white	1 cup unckd.	700
Rice, brown or white	1 cup cooked	225

VEGETABLES

Asparagus	1 cup	25
Beans		
Baked (canned)	1 cup cooked	300
Green or waxed	1 cup	25
Lentils	1 cup cooked	225
Pinto or white	1 cup cooked	225
Soybean (tofu)	1 cup	175
Soymilk, noncondensed	1 cup	75
Broccoli	1 cup	25
Carrot	1 large	50
Carrot juice	1 cup	100
Cauliflower	1 cup	25
Chard	1 cup	25
Corn, frozen	1 cup	125
Corn on cob	1 large	150
Lettuce	2 cups	25
Mushrooms	6 medium	25
Onion, celery	for seasoning	0
Peas, green	1 cup	125
Pepper, green or red	1 average	25
Potato		
French-fried	1 cup	425
Hash-browns	1 cup	350
Russet (baking)	1 medium	175
Russet (baking)	1 extra-large	275
White or red, boiled	2 medium	150
Salad, mixed vegetable	2 cups	50
Spinach	1 bunch	25
Squash		
Acorn (winter)	1/2 medium	125
Zucchini (summer)	1 cup	25
Sweet Potato	1 medium	175
Tomato	1 medium	25
Tomato juice	1 cup	50
Vegetable juice cocktail	1 cup	50
Yam	1 large	300

TABLE 5

CALORIE CHART

BREADS

All breads, not buttery	1 ounce	75
Bagel	1 large	225
Muffin, English	1 regular	150
Muffin, sweet or corn	1 medium	200
Roll, buttery	1 medium	175
Roll, reg. whole wheat	1 medium	125
Slice of bread	1 regular	75
Slice of bread	1 large	100

DAIRY PRODUCTS

Cheese		
All regular varieties	1 ounce	100
Shredded regular	1/2 cup	175
Modified lowfat	1 ounce	75
Shredded modified	1/2 cup	125
Cottage Cheese	1 cup	200
Eggs	6 jumbo whites	125
Eggs	3 whole ex. large	300
Ice cream, regular	1 cup	275
Ice cream, "gourmet"	1 cup	300
Milk, lowfat	1 cup	150
Milk, skim	1 cup	100
Sherbet	1 cup	250
Yogurt		
Frozen lowfat	1 cup	175
Frozen nonfat	1 cup	75
Nonfat, flavored	1 cup	200
Plain nonfat	1 cup	150

FATS AND OILS

Butter	1 tablespoon	100
Margarine	1 tablespoon	100
Mayonnaise	1 tablespoon	100
Pan coating, no-stick	1 sec. spray	0
Vegetable oils	1 tablespoon	125

FISH AND SEAFOOD*

Catfish	8 ounces	225
Cod	8 ounces	175
Crab	8 ounces	200
Flounder	8 ounces	175
Haddock	8 ounces	175
Halibut	8 ounces	225
Lobster	8 ounces	200
Mahi-Mahi	8 ounces	225
Perch	8 ounces	225
Salmon	8 ounces	400
Scallops	8 ounces	175
Seabass, northern	8 ounces	225
Shrimp, shelled	8 ounces	200
Snapper	8 ounces	200
Sole	8 ounces	175
Swordfish	8 ounces	275
Trout, rainbow	8 ounces	375
Tuna, fresh	8 ounces	250
Tuna, canned	6.5 ounces	225
Whitefish (roughy)	8 ounces	350

FRUIT, FRESH AND DRIED

Apple	1 medium	100
Applesauce	1 cup	125
Apricot, dried	1/2 cup	150
Apricot, fresh	3 medium	100
Avocado	1/2 medium	175
Banana	1 large	125
Cantaloupe	1/2 medium	75
Casaba melon	1 cup chunks	25
Cherry	1 cup	75
Grapes	1 cup	100
Honeydew	1 cup chunks	50
Kiwi	1 medium	50
Mango	1 medium	150
Olive, ripe	3 large	50
Orange, navel	1 large	75
Papaya	1/2 large	75
Peach	1 medium	50
Pear	1 medium	125
Pineapple	1 cup (3/4 inch slice)	75
Plantain	1 large, cooked	150
Plum	3 medium	100
Prune	1/4 cup	100
Raisin	1/4 cup	125
Raspberry, red	1 cup	75
Strawberry	1/2 pint	50
Tangerine	1 large	50
Watermelon	2 cups chunks	50

FRUIT JUICE

Apple	1 cup	125
Cranberry	1 cup	150
Grape	1 cup	150
Grapefruit	1 cup	100
Lemonade	1 cup	125
Orange	1 cup	125
Pineapple	1 cup	150
Sparklers with juice	10 ounces	125

MEATS AND POULTRY*

Beef		
Flank steak	8 ounces	325
Ground beef (8% fat)	8 ounces	400
Ground beef (15% fat)	8 ounces	525
Round steak	8 ounces	425
Sirloin steak	8 ounces	475

* All values are for uncooked lean cuts and filets, with skin and visible fat removed.

103

TABLE 5
CALORIE CHART

Chicken		
Breast, boneless	8 ounces	375
Breast, with bone	8 ounces	225
Thigh, with bone	8 ounces	275
Lamb, extra lean	8 ounces	425
Turkey		
Breast, boneless	8 ounces	350
Ground (10% fat)	8 ounces	400
Veal, cutlet	8 ounces	425

MISCELLANEOUS

Cereals		
Corn Flakes	1 cup	75
Grape Nuts	1/2 cup	275
Hot cereals	1 ounce dry	100
Oat bran	1/2 cup dry	175
Oatmeal	1/2 cup dry	150
Raisin Bran	1 cup	150
Shredded Wheat	2 large biscuits	150
Wheatena	1/2 cup dry	275
Crackers		
Rice cakes & crackers	each	25
Soda, saltine	2 squares	25
Tortilla chips	1 ounce (1 cup)	150
Lasagna	4" x 4"	450
Nuts		
Coconut	1/4 cup	75
Most raw nuts	1/4 cup	200
Most roasted nuts	1/4 cup	225
Peanut butter	1 tablespoon	75
Pistachio	25 in shell	100
Pancakes	1 6-inch diameter	150
Pizza, cheese/mushroom		
	1/8 of 12-inch pie	250
Popcorn		
Air-popped	1 cup	25
Theatre—no butter	1 cup	50
Salad dressing		
Fat-free	1 tablespoon	0
Reduced calorie	1 tablespoon	50
Regular	1 tablespoon	75
Soup		
Consomme, broth	1 cup	25
Cream-based, chowder	1 cup	125
Noodle with broth	1 cup	75
Spaghetti sauce		
Nonfat	1/2 cup	50
Regular	1/2 cup	100
Spices	all types	0

Tortilla, corn	3 average	200
Tortilla, flour	1 medium	125

RICE AND PASTA

All pastas, noodles	4 ounces dry	400
All pastas, noodles	1 cup cooked	200
Noodles	1 cup uncooked	175
Pasta shells	1 cup unckd.	250
Rice, brown or white	1 cup unckd.	700
Rice, brown or white	1 cup cooked	225

VEGETABLES

Asparagus	1 cup	25
Beans		
Baked (canned)	1 cup cooked	300
Green or waxed	1 cup	25
Lentils	1 cup cooked	225
Pinto or white	1 cup cooked	225
Soybean (tofu)	1 cup	175
Soymilk, noncondensed	1 cup	75
Broccoli	1 cup	25
Carrot	1 large	50
Carrot juice	1 cup	100
Cauliflower	1 cup	25
Chard	1 cup	25
Corn, frozen	1 cup	125
Corn on cob	1 large	150
Lettuce	2 cups	25
Mushrooms	6 medium	25
Onion, celery	for seasoning	0
Peas, green	1 cup	125
Pepper, green or red	1 average	25
Potato		
French-fried	1 cup	425
Hash-browns	1 cup	350
Russet (baking)	1 medium	175
Russet (baking)	1 extra-large	275
White or red, boiled	2 medium	150
Salad, mixed vegetable	2 cups	50
Spinach	1 bunch	25
Squash		
Acorn (winter)	1/2 medium	125
Zucchini (summer)	1 cup	25
Sweet Potato	1 medium	175
Tomato	1 medium	25
Tomato juice	1 cup	50
Vegetable juice cocktail	1 cup	50
Yam	1 large	300

CHAPTER SEVEN

Tips For Home-Cooked Meals

Here are some tips that should be helpful for your meal planning. Remember, the goal of your diet is to achieve results. There is no Puritan ethic involved where deprivation and sacrifice have some positive value of their own. The whole idea is to live a natural lifestyle that is enjoyable—something you will want to follow for the rest of your life.

Any athlete who has tried to stick to a diet knows about the problem of cheating. This can actually come from several sources. First, depending on your diet, your body may actually be trying to tell you something. There are people who experiment with extreme diets like fruit diets because they hear that fruits are low in calories and that the large volume of water in fruit will fill them up. These things are true. Yet a pure fruit diet does not provide any protein, a necessary nutrient for everyone and one that is particularly essential to the natural athlete.

In this instance your body would probably signal you, in its subtle ways, that it needed the protein you weren't giving it with this extreme diet. That piece of chicken might actually look a lot better than it did before! It is important to listen to your body carefully and give it what it needs. People who are really in tune with their bodies can actually get intuitive messages encouraging a particular class of food. This is the body's way of keeping you in good shape. Listen to it.

This is not to say, however, that you should eat everything that crosses your mind as something that would taste good. Depending on your desires, that could get you into trouble very quickly. The desire for food is wrapped up in the emotions of the individual. Your sense of taste is influenced by everything from upbringing to advertising and is not a reliable guide to what the body really needs. Foods that you had as a child may bring wonderful sensations of delight, along with remembrances of special occasions and the joys of youth. At the same time, foods that we were forced to eat as children may still ring a negative bell well into adulthood, although tastes can and do change over time.

Habit can also play a major role. Since we are all creatures of habit we tend to do things the way we have always done them, and we can get set in our ways. We may always have a muffin for a snack, or a hamburger or burrito (or even a can of tuna!) for lunch. Habits can actually hurt when considering a new diet plan, since there will usually be a bit of dislocation in your day-to-day routine and maybe some minor trauma if the new foods are seen as a deprivation. The important thing is to be able to figure out the difference between a true body need and some programmed desire that you might have. If you can figure this out, you will be well on your way to having a diet that will keep you healthy and forever natural.

It was mentioned in the Dietary Guidelines that you should divide your food consumption into four or five meals per day. This allows for more efficient digestion and assimilation and helps maintain a more constant glucose and nutrient level in the blood. Because of this guideline, diet tips are provided for five meals: pre-workout meal, breakfast, lunch, afternoon snack and dinner.

Pre-workout Meal

In order to provide for the maximum energy level during your workout without excessively diverting your body's resources to digestion and assimilation you should eat a small carbohydrate meal about an hour before your workout. Try to limit the size of this meal, so your stomach does not feel full. Studies have also shown that the high blood-glucose level that results from a big meal can actually reduce your growth hormone release during exercise, so this is another reason to keep your meal small. The author trains in the morning, so this pre-workout meal is the first meal of the day. Persons who train in the afternoon should eat the same size meal before their workout for the same reasons.

Remember to take some amino acids with your pre-workout meal, say four to eight grams (tablets). These predigested aminos will help maintain plasma amino-acid levels throughout your workout. Take another six to 12 aminos *immediately* after your workout to start the recuperation process as soon as possible.

CEREALS

Oatmeal is a classic favorite and a lowfat source of complex carbohydrates. It also hits the spot on a chilly morning when you can use something warm in your stomach. Avoid putting cream, sugar and salt on the oatmeal, however, as well as butter, of course. So how can you make your oatmeal taste good? Easy.

1. Use "old-fashioned" oatmeal, which has larger flakes. The old-fashioned variety won't dissolve into mush like the instant variety does. It may take a few seconds longer to prepare, but then you don't have to sit over the stove watching it.

2. Use apple sauce or other fruit sauces for flavor. Apple sauce is 100 percent carbohydrate, without the fat or lactose that you find in traditional oatmeal flavorings. It will also provide moisture to the oatmeal. Natural apple sauce (without refined sugar) should be used. It has half the calories of sweetened apple sauce. There are also apple-raspberry, apple-cranberry and apple-strawberry sauces on the market which can be used for variety. Or you can make your own special sauce by throwing a few pieces of fresh raspberry or strawberry into the oatmeal when you start to cook it.

3. Add dried fruits to your oatmeal. Raisins are a traditional choice and are very good. For variety try dried apricots, peaches, pineapples, apples or even papaya. Dried fruits pack a wallop when it comes to calories, so be careful to measure them so you don't throw your calorie count off. Also, remember to add a bit more water to the oatmeal, since dried fruits absorb water as they plump up.

4. Spice it up. Depending on your tastes, you could add cinnamon to most of the combinations mentioned above. Nutmeg and allspice are added sometimes. All of these spices are found in pumpkin pie. Spices do not have any calories, so use as much as you like.

There are a number of other hot cereals that can be eaten instead of oatmeal. Since variety is the spice of life, try varying your cereal to add new dimensions to your pre-workout diet. Wheatena, Cream of Wheat, Malt-o-Meal and Cream of Rice are all natural and have the same number of calories as oatmeal. There are also a variety of whole-grain hot cereals sold at health food stores and in the diet sections of supermarkets. As a general rule, the closer the grains are to their natural state the better, since they have more vitamins, minerals and fiber in them. Whole grains can also be crunchier and more interesting to the taste than the more processed commercial varieties.

Another favorite is oat bran, which recently has received a lot of publicity about its supposedly cholesterol-lowering properties. Oat bran is now available in a variety of particle sizes, ranging from almost a flake to a near powder. Oat bran has fewer calories per dry ounce than most hot cereals due to its higher fiber content.

Experiment around and see which cereals excite your taste buds the most. Remember, there is no piety in boring your tongue. Virtually all hot cereals are low in fat and sodium while high in complex carbohydrates, so there's no reason to limit yourself to one. Have a different cereal each day of the week, and spice it up differently every time. There's no excuse to be bored with your pre-workout meal!

RICE, PASTA AND BREAD

Some natural athletes like steamed rice for their pre-workout meal. Steamed rice provides a nonfat way to get the complex carbohydrates you need for your training. Try cooking up some rice with bananas and cinnamon for a change of pace.

A small bowl of pasta with a healthy sauce is another option, especially if your workout is in the afternoon. Just stay away from the cheese toppings and try to get a sauce with little or no oil in it. Pasta is a great way to get the carbohydrates you need.

You could also eat several slices of bread or toast. Be careful what you put on the bread, however. Follow the Dietary Guidelines that were mentioned earlier: cut out all fats and processed sugars. This eliminates just about every bread spread, however, except for maybe apple "butter" and the natural fruit preserves. Stay away from peanut butter, which is very high in fat. If you need to splurge, try spreading the thinnest layer you can on the bread to minimize its fat and caloric impact.

TIPS FOR AFTERNOON WORKOUTS

Many athletes go to the gym after their work in the late afternoon or evening. For these people, driving home to fix a meal may not be an option, although if you make a quick stop home to change clothes for the gym you can easily add a small meal into your schedule. If you're on the go and can't stop home, you should still have your pre-workout meal. Just follow the Dietary Guidelines. The best choice under these circumstances is probably yogurt, fruit or some type of bread, like a roll or bagel. You could also have a smoothie or other fruit juice. Avoid salted nuts, candy bars, chips and all those products you find next to the cash register at stores. A pre-workout meal is not an excuse to eat junk!

Also, depending on the climate and your type of job, you could carry your pre-workout meal around with you. A cup or two of rice or pasta will not go bad in a few hours without refrigeration, nor will a baked potato. If you have an office refrigerator, try putting this meal (and any others you pack) in the frig until you make your trip in the car. This will keep your food at its maximum freshness. If your office has a microwave you could try heating up your pre-workout meal before leaving.

Remember to eat the pre-workout meal, including the aminos, about an hour before you start working out. This includes travel time to the gym. The pre-workout meal and the post-workout aminos are two of the major "secrets" for growing naturally, so follow them religiously.

Breakfast

Breakfast is one of the most important meals of the day, especially if you work out in the morning. Traditionally a time to eat sweets and pastries, it is at breakfast that the body receives the energy it needs to get off to a good start in the day's activities. Consider that your body has just been through eight to 12 hours where it hasn't eaten much, if anything. While the metabolism does slow about 20 percent during sleep, we still burn 80 percent as many calories sleeping as we do in a sedentary awake state. The body is therefore in need of nutrition and energy to begin the day.

All the Dietary Guidelines apply to breakfast as much as any other meal. Yet it is at breakfast that people break these rules the most, rationalizing that they will burn the calories off during the day. As always, it is best to supply the body with lowfat calories that provide the nutrition your body needs. This simple statement leaves most breakfast choices by the wayside.

GET YOUR PROTEIN

Protein is an essential part of breakfast. If you work out in the morning, you need to get additional protein into your body as soon as possible to continue the recuperation process. If you train in the afternoon, you will still need breakfast protein to complete your recuperation from yesterday's workout, maintain amino-acid levels in the blood and fully rebuild your body.

Egg whites are the best source of fat-free protein. All of the fat and cholesterol in the egg are contained in the yolk—the white is pure protein. This makes it the choice of most diet-conscious athletes. Each jumbo egg contains nearly five grams of protein in its white. Think of it: all this protein with zero fat!

The best way to cook the egg white is by poaching it or scrambling it in a pan. In either case, use a no-stick spray such as Pam to coat the pan or poacher bottom instead of butter. This will significantly reduce the calories added to your food. Use Teflon-coated cookware for extra ease in cleaning.

If you find egg whites by themselves to be too bland, first try different types of seasonings and vegetable toppings. Add spices or small pieces of mushroom, onion, tomato, celery or pepper to give it that omelette taste, or add salsa. You'll never miss the yolk! This will probably satisfy you most of the time. If you hit an occasional period where you need more variety, there are several possible splurges. Keep one of the yolks in the white mixture. This will provide most of the yolk taste you are used to, just with less intensity.

Another splurge is cheese. If you are poaching the egg, stick a small cube of cheese in each cup before it starts to cook. (The smaller the better.) The cheese will melt during cooking and form a flavor burst in the middle of your poached egg. Just like an omelette! Jalapeño, sharp cheddar or swiss cheeses are good choices here because of their strong flavors, reducing the amount of cheese needed to satisfy your taste buds. Parmesan, romano or feta are also good for this purpose because they have a high ratio of flavor per gram of fat. There is also a wide variety of reduced fat and sodium cheeses on the market now in most of your favorite "flavors." If you must have cheese, try using one of these modified cheeses. You'll never taste the difference.

When scrambling your whites, try sprinkling an ounce of grated cheese on top of your eggs after they are cooked and on your plate. This will add visual interest to the eggs, as well as giving your taste buds a first crack at this new flavor variation. Putting it on top will also reduce the amount of cheese you need to satisfy your craving and will make cleaning up less of a hassle than if the cheese had been cooked in with the egg.

There really are few other options for good protein at breakfast. Most people don't eat chicken, fish or turkey in the morning, but they are an option. Also on the list of foods to avoid are the usual breakfast meats, such as bacon, ham, sausage and potted meats. These meats are usually "cured" chemically, so they should probably be avoided for this reason alone. Besides, these breakfast meats have very high saturated and unsaturated fat contents. Some 80 percent of the calories in these meats actually come from cholesterol-laden animal fats—even more for bacon. Avoid them at all costs.

BAKED GOODS

A balanced breakfast should include complex carbohydrates along with your protein. There are a wide variety of wheat-based products that are traditional breakfast favorites, including breads, bagels, rolls, muffins and pancakes. Wheat is a hearty grain full of vitamins and complex carbohydrates which can have a valuable place in most natural athletes' diets. Its long history of use around the world has led to a great number of variations in baked goods that are pleasing to the smell, taste and eye. Is it really necessary to deprive yourself of all these goodies?

There are some persons who have a sensitivity to wheat gluten which inhibits their absorption of wheat. Should you be one of these individuals, avoid wheat entirely and substitute rice- or corn-based products, since you risk possible digestive disorders by consuming wheat. Besides, the purpose of eating is to get energy material absorbed into your body for use during your training. If your system won't absorb wheat for whatever reason, why bother eating it?

The problem with baked goods in general is not the wheat, since wheat is a complex carbohydrate. The problem lies in the other ingredients that are often placed in the product, such as butter, shortening or liquid oils, sugar and salt. Just follow the Dietary

111

Guidelines when considering eating a baked good. If you are buying it in the store it is easy to look at the list of ingredients and see what has been put into the product. You can also get some idea of how healthy it is by looking at the placement of different items on the list of ingredients. Remember that these listings are by weight and not calories and that sometimes bakers will put in several different types of oils or sugars to make it seem healthier than it actually is. (In some cases, fat or sugar would be the first ingredient if they didn't resort to this trick.) Also, check the nutritional breakdown to see how many grams of fat the product contains.

The principal goal in choosing a baked good is to minimize the fat, salt and sugar content. There are baked goods which have none of these ingredients in them. Many of these products are quite good, although others take some getting used to. Also, if you are energetic and/or have a loving mother who lives locally, try baking your own goods. That way you can be sure of what the ingredients are. Experiment to find the best options for you. Remember that yeast and baking powder have few calories, so you can have light, airy breads, muffins and baked goods that meet the Dietary Guidelines as well.

Most other products on the market contain some fat, sugar and salt but in varying amounts. Just try to minimize the quantities of these ingredients in what you choose to eat, paying particular attention to fat. Most store breads have relatively little fat in them, as do most bagels (except for the cheese and egg varieties). Rolls usually have more fat so they can taste "richer." However, there are whole wheat rolls that are low in fat. All of these choices are relatively good and in moderate amounts can be a part of your diet on a regular basis.

There are also a wide variety of muffins on the market. Some of these muffins are better for your diet than others, of course, depending on the ingredients. Try to restrict yourself to those brands which are low in fats and sugars. Check the labels though, since some brands, while boasting that they don't have any cholesterol, are actually full of fats. Almost all supermarket-brand muffins contain butter or hydrogenated oils, refined sugars and possibly chemical preservatives. Avoid these types if at all possible. Your best choice, if you are industrious, is to bake your own muffins at home. Start from scratch if you can and keep to the Dietary Guidelines. Mixes are also available, some of which are quite good. Just put in less oil than they call for in the recipe.

The rest of the list of baked goods should be considered splurges. Pancakes are definitely the best choice, since they can be prepared easily at home. Try substituting some fruit juice concentrate for the oil and egg, and use a no-stick spray instead of oil to cook them. Also, try using just egg whites in the mix. (Two egg whites equal one whole egg in liquid volume.) Instead of drowning your pancakes in syrup, add some fresh fruits like blueberries or raspberries to the batter, or even apple sauce. Cinammon or nutmeg could also be added for a bit of spice.

An occasional pancake meal can be a well-deserved splurge, especially if it helps you resist the temptations of waffles, french toast, sweet rolls and croissants. These last items are chock-full of fats and sugars, so try to avoid them if at all possible. If you absolutely must have some, make it the smallest portion that will satisfy your urge, and remember to add it into your calorie count. Of course, you've used up your splurge for the day!

CEREALS

Cereals are a traditional breakfast food. If you work out in the afternoon, eat cereals for breakfast frequently. Of course, if you train in the morning, you could eat more of what you just had for your pre-workout meal, but most people would find this rather monotonous on a regular basis. Morning work-out persons should therefore try to vary their carbohydrate intake by having one or more of the other carbohydrate sources mentioned earlier, including steamed rice. Of course, if you are really on a cereal kick, there is nothing wrong with filling up on cereal. It all depends on your mood and desires.

There are a variety of cold cereals on the market which are good, and many more that are bad. As always, stay away from those that have fat and sugar in them. Definitely not on the recommended list are most granolas, which actually contain a lot of oil and sugar. Be sure to read the list of ingredients before you buy any cereal. Many cereals nowadays are vitamin-enriched to some extent, so most have about the same amount of nutrient value (not much). As long as they meet the Dietary Guidelines, go with the one that tastes best to you.

Provided you are not lactose sensitive, minimize your fat content by using only nonfat milk with your cereal. It may taste a bit watery at first, but you'll get used to it. Fruit juices are another option.

113

Lunch

Lunch is often one of the most underrated meals of the day. Many people who have daytime jobs rush through lunch as if it didn't matter at all, shoveling down anything that is quick and convenient. This may include a hamburger, hot dog, burrito or the infamous sandwich on white bread, soda and chips. These lunch choices are frequently high in fat and low on nutrients. As such, they rob your body of the opportunity for sound nutrition at the crucial midpoint of the day. The body cannot prosper on a good breakfast and dinner with nothing substantial in between. You have to *make* time for a good, nutritious lunch.

Lunch should be viewed as an opportunity to provide the body with enough complex carbohydrates to replenish your body's glycogen stores (if you train in the morning) or to fully load your muscles with energy for the workout to come (if you train in the afternoon). Providing a good portion of protein for muscle growth is also essential in a balanced lunch. A fully functional lunch will therefore have enough complex carbohydrates and protein to give your body what it needs to perform at its best.

While the quantities of food you need to consume will depend on your energy requirements and the size of your other meals, as a general rule it is wise to have a lunch which is no smaller than your dinner. In fact, your consumption of carbohydrates should be greatest in the morning and least in the evening, with lunch somewhere in between. This will give your body the carbs it needs while you are active and awake, allowing you to sleep without that bloated feeling in your stomach. Always try to have a properly sized nutritious lunch that will keep you going throughout the day. You'll find that your energy level will be higher than if you'd had the typical mini-lunch.

First and foremost, try to keep your fat consumption to a minimum. This can be harder during lunch since many people eat it in a restaurant, and the rest are trying to brownbag in the most convenient way possible. Still, with a little organization and practice, a lowfat and delicious lunch can be yours for the asking. Your body will thank you for it.

WAYS TO GET PROTEIN

Protein is a necessary part of lunch. One protein source with a low amount of fat per ounce is canned tuna fish. A can of tuna packed in water has only six grams of fat and over 40 grams of protein—one of the best protein/fat ratios around. Avoid tuna packed in oil since it doubles the calorie count per can and provides nothing additional in the way of nutrition. It is also best to buy tuna with no salt added, since this will reduce your sodium intake per can by 90 percent.

The easiest way to eat tuna is straight from the can. When eating it "au natural" it is best to buy the white-meat albacore tuna, since the taste is noticeably better. Albacore tuna is also a fish which swims deeper in the ocean than other tunas, so the nets used to capture them do not trap dolphins—unlike the yellowfin tuna caught to make the light-meat variety. Albacore is a bit more expensive, but you can rest assured that no dolphins will be killed in bringing it to your table. Flipper will be grateful!

Tuna straight out of the can is dry and hard to swallow, so have a glass of water ready. A better way to eat it is by mixing the tuna up in a salad with tomatoes, diced onions or scallions, cucumbers or pickles, celery, red or green peppers and your favorite spice blends. Since vegetables and spices have no fat in them you can let your imagination go wild with new flavor variations. You could also add some nonfat Italian salad dressing to moisten the tuna.

Remember that mayonnaise is 100 percent fat. There are now imitation mayonnaises on the market which have no eggs in them and therefore no cholesterol. These substitutes are still chock-full of fat, however, usually soybean or safflower oils. If you find the thought of tuna without mayonnaise to be intolerable, try to at least reduce the quantity of mayo you do use. A little bit goes a long way in adding flavor to your tuna, while providing enough "glue" so the tuna does not fall out when you make a sandwich. Wean yourself off of mayo slowly if you must, but try to make the effort. You could also try switching to one of the reduced fat mayonnaise substitutes, which can have half the calories of regular mayo. Plain nonfat yogurt is another option.

If you get tired of tuna, try eating chicken and turkey breast or lean beef for a change of pace. Chicken and turkey breast have around 18 grams of fat per pound, which is more than a can of tuna but a lot less than a hamburger or hot dog. Beware that dark meat chicken and turkey (thighs and legs) have nearly double the amount of fat per pound and substantially less protein. Breasts should be cooked without the skin and can be broiled, baked or even boiled if you prefer.

Try cooking up a whole batch and putting them in plastic bags for storage. This reduces the amount of preparation time per breast and makes it a lot more convenient for your lunches. Some natural athletes cook up a whole week's worth over the weekend and then refrigerate or freeze them, depending on when they're going to be eaten. You can add more variety to your chicken or turkey by adding different spices to the breasts as they bake or broil. (If you cook up a batch at one time there is no reason all of them have to have the same spices.) Also, if you are baking your breasts, try adding a bit of water and covering the pan with foil. This will keep the juices in the meat from evaporating. You could also try adding onions, bay leaves and other spices to flavor your breasts, as well as carrots, celery and potato slices for tasty vegetable treats. If you like that brown "baked" color on your breasts, take the foil off the pan for the last five to ten minutes.

The only other lunch meats that are usually consumed are delicatessen cold cuts. With few exceptions, these cold cuts have surprising amounts of fat in them. Bolognas, salamis, pastramis and the like contain moderate to high levels of fat per ounce. Some turkey-based varieties are lower than their beef counterparts, which helps things a little, but as a rule cold cuts should be avoided except on a splurge basis. Hams actually have high fat levels, so beware of advertisements that boast about low-calorie counts per slice. These advertising claims are achieved by cutting the ham into very thin slices. The fat level per ounce still remains the same. As always, try to avoid beef and cheese, since these are highest in fat content. If the urge to eat them proves irresistible, have the smallest portion that will satisfy your craving.

If a cold cut or submarine sandwich is going to be eaten, be sure to count the calories carefully. Avoid the use of mayonnaise, butter and margarine, since these will substantially increase your total calories. Also, try to use cold cuts that do not have nitrates in them. These preservatives can cause negative reactions in some persons and are not a good idea for anybody. They are added to food to increase its shelf life. Some health food stores have deli meats without preservatives. Provided they look fresh, try to buy these types of meats to fill your sandwiches. Better yet, how about some chicken or turkey breasts or a delicious can of tuna!

COMPLEX CARBOHYDRATES

Complex carbohydrates are a vital part of a balanced lunch. They provide needed energy to keep you going during the afternoon hours, when many people experience a low-energy slump period. There are many different complex carbohydrates, including potatoes, rice, beans, bread and pasta. All provide virtually fat-free calories in their natural states. The problem with these items is not the basic food itself but the toppings and flavorings people often add to them—sour cream and butter on potatoes, for example. As long as you recognize this fact and flavor them in a lowfat way, you can enjoy a wide variety of complex carbohydrates that will satisfy your palate without guilt.

POTATOES

Potatoes are an excellent source of carbohydrate. One way to make baking potatoes even easier is to bake up four or six at a time in the oven. After your spuds have cooled, put them in a plastic "zipper" bag and store them in the refrigerator. When you want one, warm it up in the microwave. The result will be a piping hot baked potato, ready to eat. Also, this method of baking in advance gives the potato a delicious "home fries" taste without the oil. If you want to reduce your total baking time, try partially cooking the potatoes in the microwave and then put them in the oven for a while to give them that crispy-skin baked texture.

When eating a potato, learn to love it without the butter, sour cream or cheese that is usually put on top. These fat-laden toppings have little to be said in their favor. Don't get caught in the logic that "there's some protein in the toppings." That's a rationalization. If you want protein, there are plenty of better ways to get it. Still, if "au natural" is too bland for you, try one of the imitation butter or sour cream flavorings, or even imitation bacon bits. They've got artificial flavors and preservatives in them, but if they help you to get over your habit of using fatty potato toppings they can be of great value.

Another option is to boil your potatoes, which adds water, and then add parsley or other spices for seasoning. You could also mash your potato with skim milk or make a stuffed potato by adding cooked broccoli for more flavor and moistness. These variations should help you kick the habit of fatty toppings. If you simply must have some, eat the smallest portion possible and make it your splurge for the day.

RICE

Rice is a favorite complex carbohydrate for natural athletes due to its ease in cooking. Some persons prefer brown rice to white because of its complex texture and higher fiber and nutrient values. These nutrients are contained in the bran and husk that have been removed from white rice. While these nutrients are of course valuable, brown rice has the drawbacks that it takes twice as long to cook, is chewier, and has slightly more fat (again contained in the bran and husk). If you eat a balanced diet you will be able to get the additional nutrients contained in brown rice from other sources. The decision on which to eat is therefore a personal one.

Rice is a snap to cook and can be kept in the refrigerator for days. It is therefore possible to cook up a big batch and store it for future use, heating up as much as you need in the microwave when the time comes. New rice cookers are on the market which make it still easier, allowing you to cook your rice and keep it warm for up to five hours without watching it.

Add diversity to your diet by alternating between brown and white rice, or by adding wild rice to your mix. You could also add onions, scallions, peas, minced vegetables or salt-free bouillon powder to your water when you cook your rice. These will give your rice more variety and taste, like a rice pilaf, and make your palate ask for more.

SANDWICHES

Sandwiches are a traditional part of the lunch meal. A sandwich is nothing more than bread with filling inside, so they can be healthy to eat as long as the filling and bread are healthy. Using the lowfat suggestions given earlier, you can create a variety of delicious sandwiches by alternating your fillings. You can also choose from the wide range of breads on the market, most of which are acceptable from the lowfat point of view. Certain types, such as egg breads, have more fat in them, but the amount per slice is not very great. There are also pita breads and bagels that have very little or no fat in them, so they are excellent choices.

Remember to look at the ingredients in the breads you buy. Many contain preservatives and other chemical additives to prolong shelf life and reduce production costs. Stay away from these types. Most supermarkets have plenty of good breads nowadays, so you won't have to make a special trip to the health food store to buy them. Also, try to stick to whole wheat and other dark breads, since these contain more nutrients. Avoid "air loaf" and similar white breads. There is simply no reason to buy these with all the other choices currently on the market.

PASTA

Pasta is another lunchtime favorite. A bowl of spaghetti with marinara or red clam sauce is a great source of carbohydrates with very little fat. There is no reason not to have pasta as long as the sauce is nonfat or lowfat. Just stay away from cream-based fettuccine sauces and the heavy doses of grated cheese that are usually put on top. These are high in fat and sodium. If you must add parmesan or romano for zing, keep the quantities low. A little bit of these strong-flavored cheeses can go a long way.

Another pasta variation that has recently become popular is pasta salad. These salads combine spices and diced vegetables with pasta for a cold luncheon treat. So far, so good. The problem with pasta salads lies in the oil that is usually added, as well as the cheeses. Minimize the use of these ingredients, or better yet, cut them out entirely. The delectable taste of the other ingredients will still come shining through. Try adding chunks of tuna or poultry to these salads to increase their protein content.

SOUPS AND SALADS

Soups and salads can be healthy lunches, but there are good and bad varieties of each. Remember that a natural athlete needs protein throughout the day to build his/her muscles, something that most soups and salads do not provide in anything near the amounts required for proper muscle growth and recuperation. If you are going to have soup or salad, enjoy it, but have a protein source along with it. This will keep your noontime meal nutritionally balanced.

The main rule on soups is to avoid the "cream of" variety, which includes New England-style clam chowder. This type of soup contains a great deal of butterfat and cholesterol. Any other type of soup is fine, especially those which are made from vegetable broth. Soups which contain chicken or beef stock have more fat than vegetable broth soups, since these meats have fat in them, but nowhere near the amount found in "cream of" soups. All other ingredients in soup, usually vegetables and noodles, are carbohydrates which can be eaten guilt-free.

If you are preparing your soup stock from scratch, make up a batch ahead of time and refrigerate it until the fat solidifies on the top. Remove this fat layer and make soup from the remaining stock. This will significantly reduce the fat content of your soup.

Salads can be nutritious and flavorful additions to your meal. All the vegetables used to make salads are very low in fat (except for olives and avocados, which are actually considered fruits) so there is no reason to restrict your intake of them. On the contrary, you can consume large volumes of these foods, satisfying your stomach's craving for something that is filling without taking in a lot of calories.

The problem with salads is the dressings usually put on them. There are oil-free dressings on the market, including the Pritikin brand, which add flavor to your greens without fat. Most dressings, however, contain large amounts of soybean or other oils. While soybean oil has no cholesterol, it is pure fat, and the calories you get from it can add up fast. If you do use a dressing with oil for some flavor variety, try picking one of the "lite" or reduced-calorie dressings, which can have half the calories of regular dressings.

Sometimes people on a diet will order salad instead of a "full" meal and then add so much dressing they would have been better off with a sandwich! Dressings are very calorie-rich, so be careful how much dressing you use. Try ordering it on the side and then dipping the tip of your fork in it before you go for a forkful of salad. Better yet, pass on the dressing completely. Also, be careful with the croutons. If they are bread squares, like melba toast, they are crunchy additions to a salad. Many croutons are dipped in oils or butter, however, to "improve their flavor." Stay away from these varieties.

Meat and seafood salads are ways to have a balanced protein and carbohydrate meal in one dish. The characteristics of the protein sources and pastas used in these salads have been discussed earlier. Just try to minimize the amount of mayonnaise that is mixed in with them. This may be difficult at a restaurant, since they probably have already made up a big batch of it, but you could ask them anyway. If you are at home, add just a little mayo (or better yet, "lite" mayo or nonfat yogurt) to moisten it. If you're not careful, the calories in the mayonnaise could wind up being more than the meat/pasta. Should the salad seem a bit dry, eat it with a tall glass of iced tea instead of adding more mayo. There are a wide variety of teas out on the market, both traditional and herbal, and all have virtually no calories. Much better for your diet!

Many athletes eat lunch at a restaurant, both for convenience and as a way to get out of the office for a while. Eating out can add great variety to your meals, but it can also set your diet back a lot if you order the wrong things. In Chapter Eight some tips for eating out wisely are discussed, including tips on ethnic restaurants. This way you will be able to enjoy the convenience and experience of trying new things without compromising your diet to any great degree.

Afternoon Snack

The afternoon snack is a smaller meal to get you through to dinner. Having a snack will help you divide your total daily food intake into five meals, as opposed to cramming all your food into the usual three meals. This will allow your body to digest food more efficiently. It will also maintain a more even blood-glucose level throughout the day, enhancing muscle recuperation and minimizing those physical up-and-down feelings. This snack can be one of several different types of food.

FRUIT

Some persons have a fruit medley, combining a variety of fruits or juices. If you're creative, each day can be a different medley, adding a welcome change of pace to your diet. All fruits (except avocados, olives and coconuts) are virtually nonfat, so there is no reason to restrict yourself to any one type. Eat as much as you like of a wide variety. Juices and juice blends are equally as good, although they are a more concentrated source of energy with less bulk and fiber per calorie. Make sure that you don't eat a lot of extremely acidic fruits like pineapple together, since these may upset your stomach. In moderation, however, you can pick and choose from the wide number of choices available. Just remember that fruits vary widely in their calorie counts.

Fresh fruits are the best, of course, but sometimes the fruit you crave is not in season. If that is the case, frozen or canned fruits are almost as good, since not too many nutrients are lost in the canning/freezing process. Try to stay away from packaged fruits that have sugar added, since the sucrose or fructrose is just empty nutrition. It can also double the number of calories per piece of fruit, especially if you drink the syrup. With today's international air freight most fruits are available fresh year-round, even if they cost a bit more when not in season. So sticking to the real fruit is usually possible. Yet if your craving is for canned peaches or some frozen strawberries, go ahead and have them. Concern yourself most with limiting your fat intake.

SNACK VARIATIONS

Other snack choices include fruit-juice sparklers, frozen fruit bars, yogurt, rice cakes and no-salt pretzels. Nonfat yogurt and frozen yogurt are also good choices for a snack. While most flavored yogurts have some sugar in them, the amounts are usually small and nothing to be concerned about. Yogurt is also one of the healthiest snacks around—far better than the other options such as cheese, nuts, chips and those store-bought baked goods like cupcakes and filled sponge cake. All of these last options should be avoided at all times. Remember, just because it's snacktime you can't throw out your diet rules.

Rice cakes are another healthy snack. These snacks are now available just about everywhere and come in a variety of flavors. Rice cakes are pure complex carbohydrate and are a great way to fill your stomach for only a few calories. They can be rather crunchy and dry, however, so have some liquid ready. Try drinking them with water or iced tea instead of juice or soda to keep the calorie count down.

Granola bars have often been advertised as a healthy alternative to more traditional snack treats. Most of the bars on the market, however, need to be investigated before you eat them. This goes for many of the baked fruit-flavored bars as well. Always look at the list of ingredients and the nutritional information for these bars. Some contain high levels of oil and fat, at times even palm kernel oil and other saturated fats.

Many health food stores and supermarkets carry brands made from whole wheat flours and dried fruits that contain only a few grams of fat per serving. These are the brands you should buy if a craving for one of these bars strikes. Avoid the more fat-laden varieties, especially the peanut-butter and chocolate-chip versions. This type of bar is low-nutrient food with a health-food label. Don't be misled.

Sometimes when you get home from a long day at work, you need a moment to relax and regroup. Traditionally, this is a time when people unwind with beer and potato chips, or maybe a martini and some mixed nuts. The psychological need for this snack is real—something that remains real even if alcoholic beverages are not consumed. (They are basically empty calories, anyway.) When you feel the need for this pre-dinner snack, try having some salt-free pretzels or one of the healthier crackers now on the market with a vegetable juice cocktail or some herbal tea. You'll find that after a few minutes you'll perk up and feel like a new person again. And since you didn't eat any fat-laden foods, your body will appreciate it as much as your mind will like the psychological lift. After all, who says a diet has to be a hassle?

Dinner

Dinner is traditionally the largest meal of the day. After a long, hard day's work, many people who have virtually starved themselves for most of their waking hours have their biggest meal—often only a few hours before bedtime. Of course, sometimes dinner is the only time you *can* relax and have a leisurely meal, especially if your work schedule is extremely active. If at all possible, however, you should try to have a large lunch and a moderately sized dinner, since this will provide your body with the carbohydrates it needs for energy during the active hours of the day.

Having a big meal right before bedtime does not make a great deal of sense from an energy efficiency point of view, since your metabolism slows during sleep and requires less energy. Therefore, if your work is fairly sedentary and you have time for a full lunch, dinner might be nothing more than a protein source and a vegetable with no complex carbohydrates at all. If you have a physically demanding job, a high metabolism or are spending a lot of time at your athletic training, however, you will need additional complex carbohydrates along with your protein and vegetable. This will allow you to take in your total caloric requirement for the day and build up your glycogen stores for tomorrow's workout. Just try to eat most of your complex carbs earlier in the day when the body needs them. This will minimize the likelihood that your body will store the calories you take in as fat.

FISH

Dinner should always consist of a protein source. The lowest protein-to-fat ratios are found in fish, so this is your best source of protein. Since dinner is such an important meal, fresh fish is in order if your budget will permit. Just remember that not all fishes are created equal when it comes to fat per pound. In fact, the amount of fat can vary radically, from 3 grams per pound (gr./lb.) in cod to 65 gr./lb. in salmon. The fishes which are lowest in fat content are the following: cod, haddock, halibut, red snapper and sole. Scallops and shrimp are also very low in fat.

Swordfish has as many grams of fat per pound as chicken breast (18 gr./lb.). Mackerel is even higher. Curiously, seabass can vary widely in fat content. The Chilean variety (which is pure white) is extremely high in fat, while other varieties of sea bass (which are reddish in color) are quite low in fat content. Avoid salmon except as a splurge. It has as much fat as a round steak.

Fish can be prepared in a variety of ways. It can be broiled, baked or stir-fried. When broiling, never add butter. Shake on one of the wide variety of salt-free seasonings available on the market. There are at least 15 of these spice blends currently sold. To keep the fish and spices from drying out, squeeze some lemon or tomato juice over the fish after you have added the spices. This will keep everything nice and moist. With all the different spice variations and types of fish on the market, you could eat fish every night for a month and never have the same dinner. Always aim for variety!

Fish can also be baked. Certain types of fish, like sole, have a lot of water in them and can be baked on an open tray, while others, such as halibut, need to be covered to retain moisture. You can bake fish much as you broil it, with seasonings and lemon or lime juice. For a nice flavor variation, try covering the fish with foil and adding a variety of chopped vegetables and fresh spices in with the fish. Mushrooms, peppers, onions, celery, tomatoes and carrots are excellent choices for cooking with baked fish. Also, try giving it that personal touch with some fresh cilantro, parsley, sage or thyme. Also, if you like your fish browned somewhat, take the foil off the fish for the last five minutes that it's in the oven. This will evaporate some of the juices from the vegetables and turn the fish a nice golden brown.

You can also stir-fry fish either in a wok or frying pan. Since fish has a lot of water in it you will usually not need to add oil to cook it, especially if you keep the heat on medium. Cut the fish into cubes to speed the cooking process. The vegetables you add, especially mushrooms, also contain a great deal of water and make it easy to cook without oil. Try covering the fish/vegetables for a few minutes at the beginning. This will allow them to steam and keep them from sticking. After the water has come out of the ingredients, you can take the cover off and stir them until done.

In certain instances you may want to add some tomato or vegetable juice cocktail to the pan, or use a no-stick spray, to make sure nothing does sticks. This may happen with some drier fishes, especially if you don't cover them at the beginning. You could also put a teaspoon full of sesame oil in the wok to make your meal an exciting oriental taste treat. This modest splurge will add a few calories to your meal but a great deal of flavor. Any vegetable that pleases your palate could also be added, including scallions or green onions to follow through on the oriental theme. If you do use oil, brown your vegetables in it for a while, then add the fish.

Unlike chicken, turkey and beef, where there is just one type to choose from, there are many varieties of fish available. This should provide you with enough variation to let you stick to your very lowfat regimen. Still, there may be times when the thought of eating another piece of fish becomes burdensome at best.

CHICKEN, TURKEY AND BEEF

In these instances it is best to have some chicken, turkey or beef. Just remember that the fat content is usually higher and, as a result, the same size piece of meat will have a lot more calories than an equivalent amount of fish.

White-meat poultry is always the best choice due to its lower fat content. Chicken breast has 18 grams of fat per pound, while chicken thigh has 34. There is a similar differential with turkey. As a result, always eat chicken and turkey breast. It will cost a bit more, but that's because it's more in demand. It is definitely better for you. Isn't your body worth it?

The amount of fat in beef and veal depends on the cut. As a general rule, the tougher the cut, the lower the fat content. Marbled steaks can have 110 to 170 grams of fat per pound, and nearly half of this total is saturated fat. A lean flank steak, on the other hand, can have as little as 26 grams of fat per pound. Veal is usually less than beef, ranging from 30-60 gr./lb.. Always remove all visible fat and marbling. If that means you have to throw away a quarter of the meat you buy, so be it. Beef is cheaper than fish nowadays, so don't be stingy. Cut off all the fat you can see. Also, try to stay away from pork and lamb, since these meats have even higher fat contents per pound. If you absolutely must have these meats, use the loin portions or cut out the center of the chops before cooking them. This will reduce the amount of fat and cholesterol you take in significantly.

Chicken, turkey and beef can be cooked much the same way as fish: either broiled, baked or stir-fried. Just follow the same suggestions that were given for fish. This should provide you with all the variety you need in your diet.

TOFU

Another possible source of protein is tofu. Tofu is made from soybeans and contains incomplete protein, so remember to eat tofu with grains such as rice or breads. Tofu tastes great when mixed with onions and spices in a tofu salad. The main difficulty with tofu is that it contains large amounts of fat. In fact, 50 percent of the calories in tofu come from fat. This may be surprising, since tofu is a relatively low-calorie food, but it is due to the oil in the soybeans. Being a vegetable product, however, it does not contain cholesterol. If you want a small amount of tofu, go ahead and have it. Just be aware of its fat content and restrict its use accordingly. Also, be sure that any tofu salad you buy does not contain mayonnaise. Tofu has enough fat without adding more!

CARBOHYDRATES

If you need to have a serving of complex carbs with dinner to reach their total calorie count for the day, you could have a portion of rice, potatoes, pasta, bread or beans. Many of these carbohydrates have already been discussed in the Breakfast and Lunch parts of this chapter, so you should refer to these sections for greater information. Rice, of course, can be served plain, in a pilaf or as a casserole with tomato sauce and seasonings. Potatoes can be baked or even boiled with parsley added for extra flavor.

There are so many flavors and shapes of pasta nowadays that you could have a different type every day of the week. These variations include spinach, artichoke and tomato flavors and all kinds of shapes, from spirals and noodles to wagon wheels. There are also whole wheat pastas and so-called corn pastas for persons with a sensitivity to wheat gluten. Fresh pastas are also available in a variety of shapes and flavors. Just remember to use a lowfat or nonfat sauce on your pasta.

A number of breads make good dinner selections. Cornbread can provide a great change of pace and, depending on the ingredients, can be relatively low in fat. Be sure to check the nutritional information if you're buying it at the store. You could also bake up a batch at home with one of the mixes available. Biscuits are easy to bake, as are whole wheat rolls. For variety you could heat up a sourdough or french loaf of bread in the oven and serve it piping hot for dinner. This is a great way to make dinner special.

Baked beans are another complex carbohydrate that goes well with dinner. Most canned varieties have lots of salt and pork fat in them, but there are no-salt and lowfat varieties sold at many health food stores. You could also boil up your own beans at home (either pinto, kidney, white or black) and season them to your liking with tomatoes, onions, celery and other vegetables and spices. Split peas and black-eyed peas can be cooked up in the same way. Soak your beans or peas for several hours in water to allow them to take up moisture. This will reduce their cooking time significantly.

Baked beans can provide a nice change of pace for your taste buds. If you cook up a big batch of beans, they will keep in the refrigerator for over a week and can be easily reheated on the stove or in the microwave. Depending on your appetite for beans, you could also freeze part of them for future use. However, stay away from re-fried beans (either canned or fresh), since they contain oil or even lard. Adding fat to a perfectly good bean is pointless.

VEGETABLES

Along with your starchy complex carbohydrates you should also have a vegetable. Since all vegetables are virtually nonfat, there is no reason to restrict yourself in eating them. Vegetables are also the best natural sources of vitamins and minerals, so eat all you like! Each vegetable has its own composition of nutrients, however, so it's best not to pick one or two to the exclusion of all others. Of course, stay away from butter and margarine. There is no reason to mask the great flavor of vegetables with a fatty coating.

CHEESE DISHES

Remember to stay away from cheese dishes, such as soufflé, cheese enchiladas and macaroni and cheese. These dishes contain large amounts of fat in the form of whole milk, butter and cheese and can be major diet-busters if you're not careful. If you absolutely must have cheese, use it as a garnish. Try boiling up some macaroni and sprinkling a bit of cheese on top, such as parmesan, romano or cheddar. This will give you most of the flavor you crave at a fraction of the calories. Also, try using lowfat hoop cheese or dry-curd cottage cheese.

If your taste buds demand a soufflé, try a spinach soufflé, which has somewhat fewer calories. It still has all the cholesterol and calories of the eggs and milk, however, so the difference is small. If you absolutely must have one of these dishes, enjoy a small portion and consider it a splurge. This will reduce the amount of fat you consume.

DESSERTS

If you get a craving to have dessert, try to satisfy your "need" with a lowfat alternative. Fruits, of course, are best. If they are not sweet or rich enough for you, a fruit-based dessert, like an apple pie or a tart, has less fat than chocolate pie or cheese cake. Also, remember that most of the calories in pie are in the crust, which is all shortening and flour. Try eating just the filling and leave the crust. You could even buy a fruit or pumpkin pie filling at the store and eat it without a crust at all.

Following this same reasoning, it is better to eat chocolate mousse than a chocolate mousse pie. Also, if ice cream is your idea of a dessert, try substituting ice milk, frozen yogurt or, even better, nonfat frozen yogurt. Minimize the fat content in the toppings you choose, or opt for the undiminished taste of frozen yogurt without the topping. These general rules can be applied to any dessert. Let common sense be your guide, and you will do fine. Just keep your portions small. Remember, all things in moderation!

This diet may take some getting used to, depending on your previous eating habits. If it seems a bit intense for you, then ease into it, modifying a few things in your regular diet each week. Soon, you will be living by the Dietary Guidelines without any effort at all.

CHAPTER EIGHT

Tips For Eating Out

One of the finer pleasures in life is eating out in a restaurant, savoring new flavors in an exciting atmosphere that is different from your dining room at home. Eating out is a great change of pace that can reduce the monotony of your routine and make any day something special. Lunch in a restaurant can also get you out of the office, reducing your tension and stress levels while giving you a chance to take in some fresh air. It can also give you new ideas for fixing dishes at home and expand your horizons with new flavor variations. Yet eating the wrong things in a restaurant can set your diet back significantly. It is also more difficult to estimate the calories in your food, since you obviously aren't going to take a scale into the restaurant. Does this mean that you have to give up the pleasures of eating out? Hardly. By following a few simple rules, you can still enjoy many of the positive feelings of a meal away from home without dealing a fatal blow to your diet.

The most important thing to remember is that a food dish is nothing more than a combination of individual food items. This may sound simplistic, but many people attribute special qualities to a prepared dish that lead them to overestimate its caloric value. If you go to a Chinese restaurant, for example, and order a chicken and broccoli, the calories in this dish will come from chicken, broccoli, the oil for cooking and probably the steamed rice you had along with it. Keep in mind that spices do not have calories. This is important to remember with hot or spicy dishes, since many people feel that something that is spicy must be "rich" and therefore full of fat. Not necessarily.

Break down your meal into its different food items, and simply add up all the calories in each. This is best done while you are at the restaurant, since the food will be in front of you and your estimates will be the most accurate. Just add it up in your head or use a paper napkin. If this gets in the way of your conversations with friends, or takes away from the specialness of the moment, just remember what you ate and figure out the calorie totals when you get home. It may sound complex, but after a few meals you'll get the hang of it. Remember, you're just trying to get an estimate that can help you reach your training goals.

In the chapter **More on Diet and Nutrition** a calorie chart was provided for most of the common foods. Tear out one of these charts and stick it in your wallet or purse for easy reference. After a while, you'll probably find that you've memorized the calories in the foods you commonly eat.

Take, for example, our chicken and broccoli. The average chicken breast has about four ounces of meat on it, or 175 calories. If there is less than a whole chicken breast in your meal (which is probable at most Chinese restaurants) figure 150, 125 or 100 calories accordingly. Most vegetables are around 50 calories per average portion. Rice is 225 per cup. You know how much a cup is, so figure how many cups, or fractions of a cup, you ate with your meal. Then add in the oil. If a meal has been prepared with oil but does not seem greasy, figure there is a tablespoon of oil in it, or 125 calories. If it seems greasy, figure two tablespoons and 250 calories, or even three if the portion is large. If there are more than three tablespoons full of oil per serving in your meal, you shouldn't be eating it. Pick something else on the menu.

In our hypothetical chicken and broccoli example, there is probably one tablespoon of oil in it (125 calories), between two and three ounces of chicken (125), a cup of rice (225) and a lot of broccoli (75). Throw in a fortune cookie at 25 calories, and your total meal count is 575 calories. You can do this type of calculation for any meal—it's a snap.

The Dietary Guidelines for eating out are the same as for eating at home. Minimize your fat consumption, especially saturated fats. Eat mainly complex carbohydrates and proteins. Enjoy all the vegetables and spices you like. These general rules work across the board for all types of restaurants.

Breakfast

It can be a bit of a challenge to follow the Dietary Guidelines while eating breakfast in a restaurant. Most of the choices have a lot of fat in them, including many of the traditional favorites. Still, by making small variations in the things you order, you can improve the dietary composition of your breakfast considerably.

If you are ordering eggs, tell the waiter to use just egg whites or an egg substitute like Egg Beaters. Many restaurants will agree to poach egg whites or cook up an egg white omelette. You can also order scrambled egg whites. In each case, the only fat in your food will be from the oil or butter used to keep the pan from sticking. You could even ask them to go light on the oil. Stuff your omelettes with spinach, tomatoes, peppers, mushrooms or shrimp—all of which are nonfat—and stay away from the cheese. Also, avoid those fat-laden breakfast meats like bacon, ham and sausage.

There are a number of healthy side orders that can serve as meal substitutes if you're not very hungry. Any type of bread or toast is a good source of complex carbohydrates. The same is true for bagels, English muffins, biscuits and some rolls. Just don't add butter. If bare toast is too boring, try using jelly, honey or marmalade to add flavor. When these options don't "do the trick," opt for cream cheese instead of butter. Cream cheese, while it still has a great deal of fat, at least has more protein in it than butter and fewer calories.

Another option is hot and cold cereals. Oatmeal is available at almost every restaurant, as are many of the popular cold cereals. When enjoying cereal, ask for nonfat milk, or lowfat if nonfat is not available. This will reduce your calorie count significantly. Stay away from most granolas, however, since they are prepared with oil.

If you feel like splurging, have a short stack of pancakes. Just stay away from the butter, and substitute fresh fruit for the usual syrup. You could also eat a muffin instead. Try to avoid the usual assortment of waffles, french toast, sweet rolls and pastries, all of which are high in sugar and fat. For additional breakfast suggestions, refer to the Breakfast section of **Tips for Home-Cooked Meals**.

American Fast Food

Fast-food restaurants are responding to the increasingly healthy diets of most Americans. Traditionally the home of hamburgers and fries, many of these restaurants (especially the franchises) are adding more nutritious items to their menus every year. It is these items that you should order when you are in a rush or are traveling and have no alternative on where to eat.

While fish is a lowfat food when eaten by itself, every fast food restaurant seems to serve their fish fried. This makes it worse than the chicken dishes unless, of course, the chicken is fried too. Try ordering a skinless broiled chicken sandwich if they have one. These sometimes come on whole wheat buns with lettuce and tomato and are actually quite nutritious. Some restaurants also have chicken burritos, soft chicken tacos or fajitas, which usually use chicken that has been stewed with vegetables or stir-fried. These sandwiches make interesting flavor variations. Forget about the hamburgers, cheeseburgers and all those beef-based specialty sandwiches, however, since these contain high amounts of fat.

If the restaurant has a baked potato, make this your nonfat carbohydrate selection. Biscuits are almost as good. Just don't add butter or other fatty toppings. Many fast-food outlets nowadays also have salad bars or sell ready-made salads, most of which are low-calorie and fat-free, provided you don't add the dressing. Oriental chicken salads fall into this category, as long as they don't have those fried wonton pieces in them. Avoid the salad dressings.

Between the chicken, potato and salad you can have a nutritious meal at most fast-food restaurants. Try to stay away from the fries, shakes and those high-fat desserts, however. If all this sounds rather restrictive, it is. The best recommendation of all for the natural athlete is to avoid fast-food restaurants entirely and try one of the other types of food mentioned in this chapter. All of these restaurants have menu selections that are delicious and far better for you than the typical fast-food fare.

Chinese

Chinese food offers a wonderful variety of flavors with relatively little fat. Cantonese food has a moderate amount of spices in it, while Szechuan is a lot spicier. (Remember, spices have no calories.) The Chinese use a lot of vegetables, noodles and rice in their food, which are excellent for your diet. The only problems lie in the meats and the fats used to cook some dishes.

Most Chinese restaurants seem to use chicken thigh instead of chicken breast. Be sure to ask whether thigh or breast is being used, since some waiters seem to feel that all chicken is "white meat." If the waiter says their chicken is "mixed," be careful, since it seems that the mix is always thigh and leg instead of breast and thigh. You can also ask for scallops, shrimp or seafood, all of which have a lot less fat in them, unless of course they're fried.

Stay away from fried rice, since it has lots of oil and whole egg in it. Rice absorbs large amounts of oil, so the fat content is likely to be high even if it doesn't seem greasy. Fried rice also has lots of high-sodium soy sauce in it, so it has two strokes against it. Sweet and sour dishes often contain meat that has been dipped in batter and fried, so ask first. Some restaurants stir-fry their sweet and sours, but not many. Also, fried foods like egg rolls and egg foo yung are high in fat, so stay away from them. If possible, ask for your food without MSG (monosodium glutamate). Most of the better Chinese restaurants nowadays either don't use MSG or will agree to your request to not add it to your food.

What does this leave for Chinese food? Most of the stir-fried meat and vegetable dishes. Moo goo gai pan is an excellent choice. It has lots of vegetables and chicken in a mild non-greasy sauce. Any other dish combining meat or seafood with broccoli or mixed vegetables is also good. There are a wide variety of lowfat sauces, including Szechuan garlic sauce, which can be added to any vegetable and meat combination.

Most Chinese soups are also lowfat, including hot and sour soup. These soups are thickened with a bit of rice or corn starch, so the thickness is not indicative of their fat content. Egg drop soup is made mostly from egg whites, so it is also good, as is noodle-laden won-ton soup. (Some won tons are stuffed with pork, however, although the amount is usually not great). If you are really hungry, order an extra portion of steamed rice instead of a fried appetizer or dessert. That way you can have the calories you need without the fat.

French

French restaurants are renowned for their sauces. Unfortunately, most of these are heavy on the fat. Hollandaise-type sauces are loaded with egg yolks and butter, so avoid these sauces if at all possible. You could also order the sauce on the side so you can control the quantity you eat, much like a salad dressing. The best choices at a French restaurant are the dishes with wine-flavored sauces, such as bordelaise, which have far fewer calories and fat. You could also try to order steamed or poached fish instead of the fried varieties, or chicken if fish is not available. Salads are a low-calorie alternative, such as a nicoise salad, but be careful about the dressing or walnut oil that may be added.

Also, stay away from the quiche and duck dishes, since these are loaded with fats. You might try a bouillabaisse instead, a soup made with fish and vegetables. If you are in a mood to experiment, try ordering one healthy dish with a not-so-healthy one and split them with your dining partner. This at least reduces the amount of fat you will be taking in.

Greek

Greek food can be high in fat, especially if it's made from lamb, but there are several choices that will let you savor the atmosphere of a Greek restaurant without guilt. Instead of lamb or beef, try a chicken shish-kabob, which has fewer calories and saturated fat. Order some rice and maybe some Greek salad to go along with it, and your diet will be fine. If you order salad, ask for the dressing on the side as always. The feta cheese in most Greek salads does contain some fat, but less than most cheeses. Its strong flavor can liven up a salad with relatively little fat. Avoid anchovies and Greek olives, however, since they are extremely oily and contain high amounts of fat and sodium. Another possibility is plaki, a fish and vegetable dish that is nice and spicy.

Greek desserts are tasty, but very high in fat and sugar. Baklava and other goodies contain nuts and phyllo dough, which is flaky because of its incredibly high fat content. Skip dessert entirely or take it home if you must and divide it into a couple of servings. Better yet, have some pita bread along with your meal to fill up. Pita bread is low in fat and a great way to get complex carbohydrates.

Indian

Asian Indian restaurants can now be found in most of the larger metropolitan areas. Since the Indians are by and large vegetarians, many of their dishes are meatless. Most restaurants do have a chicken tandoori, however, which is baked in a clay oven so that most of the fat drips off. It is often served with chutneys and a variety of spicy sauces. Chicken curries are another way to get protein and savor Indian food at the same time. There are also chicken dishes like tikka masala, which is marinated in yogurt and cooked with herbs and spices. Avoid lamb dishes, however, due to their higher fat content.

Another option is to eat some protein before or after you go to an Indian restaurant and fill up on carbohydrates while you are there. This way you can savor all of their vegetarian dishes and still get the protein you need for your training. There are a variety of spicy taste treats which are low in fat. Particularly good are saag paneer (made with spinach), baingan bharta (eggplant), aloo mattar (potatoes and peas), daal makhani (lentils) and chana masala (chickpeas).

Try these along with some rice pillau, a spicy Indian rice pilaf. There is also a traditional bread called naan, which is similar to pita bread and low in fat. Sometimes they put a spoonful of oil on top of it, however, so request it without oil. Try dipping your naan in raita, a non-sweet yogurt sauce with herbs. For "dessert," try a llasi, which is a yogurt and fruit-based drink that can be ordered with or without sweetener. All of these dishes are low in fat and a definite treat for your palate. When the thought of eating another bowl of plain steamed rice seems, well, boring, experiment with Indian food. It will really wake up your taste buds.

Italian

Italian food can be a great addition to your diet, provided you are careful with the cheese and fats. Most Italian meals utilize pasta in some form, either as part of the main dish or as a side dish. Pasta, as was mentioned earlier, is a very lowfat carbohydrate. Provided you eat it with a marinara sauce or other tomato-based lowfat sauce, there is no reason not to fill up on pasta to your heart's content (as long as you don't exceed your calorie count for the day, of course). You could also order the sauce on the side and only add the amount you want.

Try a wine-based sauce, like a marsala, for a change of pace. Pesto-flavored sauces are fairly lowfat as well, as are many clam-based sauces. Pasta primavera, a mixture of cooked vegetables and pasta, is another good choice, provided that not too much oil has been used in its preparation. Just remember to avoid sauces that have cream, butter and cheese in them, like an alfredo sauce. High-fat meat sauces should also be avoided.

Pizza has got to be everyone's idea of the quintessential splurge. When you ask most natural athletes what they are going to eat right after a competition, more will say pizza than any other food (although ice cream comes up a close second!) The problem with pizza is not the crust, which is just bread after all, nor the tomato sauce, which is lower in calories per ounce than the bread. The problem, once again, is the cheese. Ask the chef to go light on the cheese, or better yet, order a vegetarian special without cheese. Never order double cheese. Also, stick with toppings like mushrooms, peppers and fresh tomatoes. Stay away from pepperoni and other meat-based toppings, which add even more fat to your pizza. If you must have pizza with cheese, try to eat only a few slices. Order a take-out box for what you don't eat and freeze it when you get home. Then you can thaw it out a slice or two at a time as your splurge for the day. Pizza heats up very quickly in the microwave, however, so be careful.

If a few slices of pizza don't fill you up, try having a mixed green salad. This will fill your stomach with carbohydrates—not more fat. As always, stay away from dressings entirely or order them on the side and use them gingerly. Also, stay away from garlic bread and breaded or fried foods like veal and chicken cutlets. These are major diet-busters. Meatballs and sausages are high in fat as well. Skip them entirely. If you don't get enough protein from your Italian meal, try eating a chicken breast or take a few aminos. These are far better choices for protein than high-fat cheeses and sausages.

Japanese

By and large, Japanese cuisine is very healthy. The foods that have been recommended so often in these pages—fish and rice—are staples of the Japanese diet. Whether you like your fish raw, like sushi and sashimi, or cooked in a soup or other dish, you can be sure of getting your necessary proteins and carbohydrates with a very low fat content. The Japanese also have nonfat rice, wheat and buckwheat pastas as well as ramen noodle products, often used in soups. You can therefore explore Japanese food with relatively little restraint.

If fish is not to your liking, try a chicken teriyaki, which is chicken covered with a tangy sweet sauce. Add some steamed rice for a side dish and maybe some traditional nonfat pickled cucumbers and you will have a fairly lowfat and delicious meal. Stay away from their fried foods, such as tempuras. These batter-covered meats and vegetables have high fat contents, as you would expect. Their traditional miso soup is high in sodium, as are many of their snack foods, but as an occasional treat they are perfectly fine. Japanese food can therefore be an ideal choice for your diet when you are eating out.

Mexican

Mexican food can be high in fat, so it takes a bit of work to eat Mexican and still keep to your diet. It's possible, however. Corn tortillas, a staple in the Mexican diet, are actually quite good for you. They consist of ground corn (a nonfat carbohydrate), lime, a bit of salt and water. The problem with corn tortillas lies in the oil that is often used to cook them for certain dishes. If you can, order your taco with a soft tortilla instead of the fried shell. Stay away from tostadas and tortilla chips for the same reason. Also, stay away from flour tortillas. These cousins to the corn tortilla are prepared with fat, frequently lard, and should therefore be avoided when at all possible.

Your selection of fillings should follow the same rules mentioned earlier in this chapter. Fish tacos are now available but are usually fried, so be careful. Chicken is the next best choice. Chicken tacos or burritos are often prepared with tomatoes, onions and spicy seasonings and can be a healthy alternative. Try to stay away from beef and cheese fillings, since their fat content is high. Also, if you want a bit more zing in your taco or burrito, order some tomato-based salsa. Stay away from the sour cream, however.

Rice is a good choice to fill up on, although some seasoned rices have oil in them. If it looks or tastes like a Chinese fried rice, skip it and ask for white rice. Beans can be another good carbohydrate selection, as long as they haven't been cooked or refried with lard. Ask the waiter how they've been cooked if you're at the restaurant for the first time. Many Mexican restaurants also serve a green salad. If you need to fill up on something, try a salad with some corn tortillas and salsa. Some Mexican restaurants also serve cooking bananas, called platanos or machos. These sweet treats are low in fat as long as they aren't fried. Ask beforehand. They are also available in many supermarkets, so you could bake or boil them at home for a sweet carbohydrate treat.

Many parts of the United States now have Mexican flame-broiled chicken restaurants. These fast-food restaurants are a sensible alternative to most traditional Mexican restaurants, and some are even certified by the American Heart Association for their lowfat menus. As always, order white-meat chicken, which has less fat than the thigh or leg, along with corn tortillas. Side orders can be evaluated according to the standard Dietary Guidelines. And order as much salsa as you like!

Thai

Thai restaurants are now becoming popular in many parts of the country. Depending on the particular restaurant, Thai food can have less fat than Chinese food. There are a number of meat and vegetable combination dishes, as well as curry and mint/chili dishes. Noodle dishes are also popular, some of which are low in fat. Others are heavy on the oil, however, especially pah thai.

There are several broth-based spicy soups that are relatively low in fat and very tasty. Just skip the tom kah gai, which is a coconut chicken soup. It's very good but, like all products with coconut milk, is very high in saturated fats. If you are unfamiliar with a certain item on the menu, ask the waiter. You can also request that they use minimal oil in preparing a dish. While every chef has his/her own idea of what lowfat is, this request usually gets you a dish with less oil than if you hadn't asked at all. Most restaurants are glad to accomodate the diet-conscious customers of today!

Other Nationalities

The people of our planet have come up with an amazing variety of food dishes to delight the senses. While it is beyond the scope of this book to mention them all, you should experiment with the great diversity around you. Being on a diet does not mean you have to lock yourself up in your house and eat salad the rest of your life. Explore new taste treats. Savor the richness of the different cultures from around the world. Just don't use it as an excuse to blow your diet. Follow the Dietary Guidelines whenever you eat out. You will find that every nation has some foods that are healthier than others. Stick with those dishes and you will be doing just fine. After all, what do you think natural athletes in Africa, Korea and Peru do? If a dish has a bit of fat in it, fine. Let that be your splurge for the day.

The mental and psychological rewards of trying new foods and experiencing new flavors will add enjoyment to your life and probably help your training accordingly. And if a certain meal is more than a minor splurge, just commit to riding the bike for an extra half-hour or swimming a few extra laps. Dieting has to be fun, or one day you'll stop doing it. And that would be a pointless mistake. So enjoy your meals out, and let the pleasure you receive from these experiences reinforce the commitment to your training diet. In this way you will not only be in top shape for that competition but also have a body that is forever natural and fat-free. Enjoy!

CHAPTER NINE

The Eight Training Principles

Even though the specific exercise program you choose will depend on your sport and the goals you have set for yourself, there are certain principles which are common to all weight-training routines. Use of these principles will allow you to achieve the greatest benefit from your workout. Natural powerlifters, wrestlers and swimmers, who use weight training to gain strength for their competitions, will find that a training routine based on the eight principles will maximize their strength gains. Natural bodybuilders who follow these principles will increase their strength and muscle mass, allowing them to look their best on the posing dais. All of these training principles are interrelated. The eight most important principles are: full range of motion, intensity, goalsetting, visualization, variation, discipline, balance and safety.

Full Range of Motion

Every muscle has the ability to move through a certain range, or distance, at a specific joint angle. In order to get the greatest benefit from an exercise it is essential that each and every repetition move through the muscle's full range of motion in perfect form—not 70 percent of the range, not even 90 percent. Maximal muscle stimulation can occur only when all of the sarcomeres in the muscle fibers are brought into action—when the muscle is fully stretched and then fully contracted.

Earlier we noted that muscle hypertrophy is the result of increases in the thickness and number of filaments within the sarcomeres. It also results from the creation of additional sarcomeres within the muscle fibers. Therefore, the greatest adaptations (responses) to training can occur only when all of the sarcomeres are fully stimulated. The way to get the greatest benefit from each set and repetition of an exercise is to make sure that the weight passes through the muscle's full range of motion. This will ensure the greatest gains in strength and muscle mass.

It's not as easy as it sounds. There is a big difference in the amount of weight you can lift at 90 percent of full range and at 100 percent. Trying to lift a weight through that final 10 percent can be difficult, since there is a tendency for the weight to "stick" at the bottom. That is why so many people cheat and only do 90 percent of full range: so they can do more repetitions at higher weights. This technique may boost their egos but does little to stimulate natural muscle growth.

Hypertrophy is achieved by utilizing the muscle's full range of motion, even if that means you have to temporarily lower the weight to do the exercise in correct form. Of course, once you have perfected the technique and muscle growth occurs you will be able to lift more weight, eventually doing the same weight you did before (or even more) but now with excellent form. And you'll have bigger, stronger muscles to show for it!

Proper form is a constant requirement for achieving your goals naturally. It is important to use the correct form throughout the entire range of motion—even during those first, easy repetitions. Nothing will be gained by bouncing or cheating a weight up. Swinging your body back and forth to force up a weight that is too heavy will not stimulate muscle growth, either. You need to concentrate on your performance of the exercise, slowly moving through the entire range of motion with precision and care. Don't gyp yourself by stopping short of a full stretch and contraction. There's no reason to be in a hurry. Make each repetition count! Focus your thoughts on the individual muscle and isolate the movement of that muscle in your mind. This attention to detail will keep you from cheating and help assure the greatest muscle stimulation.

Intensity

Intensity is a key way to achieve natural strength gains and muscle growth. As was noted earlier, hypertrophy takes place when the muscle is overloaded. This overload occurs when there is an increase in one or all of three factors: duration, frequency and intensity. Duration is the amount of time you spend actively training a bodypart each time you work out. Frequency is the number of times you train a bodypart per unit of time, say, per week or month. (These concepts are discussed in the next chapter.) Intensity is technically a measure of the resistance and velocity of the movement. Therefore, the more weight or speed that is used during an exercise, the greater the muscle's power output and the greater the intensity.

The way to achieve peak intensity is to constantly strive for a maximal muscle contraction. This means using the highest amount of weight (resistance) that the muscle is capable of handling with proper form. Studies have shown that the greatest hypertrophy of the fast-twitch muscles is achieved with sets of four to eight repetitions. The slow-twitch muscle fibers, on the other hand, grow the most when the sets consist of 12 to 20 repetitions. However, *every* set should be performed to failure, that is, until you are no longer able to do another repetition using all of your muscular strength and will power.

Don't stop just because you've reached your initial goal of, say, eight repetitions. Continue until complete failure of the bodypart and, if at all possible, get a spotter to help you so you can force out a few additional repetitions. If you consistently do more than the number of repetitions you have set as your goal, it's time to increase the amount of weight you lift. Remember that it is the muscle's contraction against a resistance it is unaccustomed to that causes the physical changes resulting in hypertrophy and increased strength.

Many factors will determine your intensity level, including your motivation, goal orientation, confidence level and drive. Intensity is really independent of your strength, although some people confuse the two concepts. A beginner who lifts 20-pound dumbbells, using every bit of drive and determination he or she can muster, has a higher level of intensity than a larger or more developed athlete who lifts 30-pound dumbbells with a nonchalant "what-me-worry" attitude. Won't the more "advanced" athlete be surprised when the beginner's intensity level stimulates so much muscle growth that he or she starts lifting 35-pound dumbbells, passing our athlete up!

The intensity you achieve is dependent on your mindset. The act of lifting a weight is a simple case of mind over matter, in which the mind sends neural impulses to the motor units in the muscle, ordering them to lift the weight in question. As a result, the amount of weight you can lift is largely determined by the amount you *think* you can lift. This is the major reason why natural athletes of the same height and body type can lift widely varying amounts of weight. The boundaries of individual accomplishment are set by the person's self-esteem.

You need to believe in yourself and in your ability to reach the goals you have set. Total confidence is essential. Only when you are confident of your direction in life will you be able to rise from the mass of competitors and soar to your true potential. It is not enough to believe that you *may* get stronger. You have to believe that you *will* get stronger—just as the sun rises every day. Rather than letting yourself fall victim to negative thoughts, block them out and keep yourself full of positive mental programming. Don't take no for an answer!

Of course, no human being is ever 100 percent positive. Yet within the limits of reality you can set a positive course for your training and then by and large stick to it. The self image each of us has determines what we can and cannot do. If this self image is expanded, a whole new range of opportunities opens up: higher achievement in sports, more success in your career, etc. The choices are personal, but the methodology is the same for everyone.

Believe in yourself and 90 percent of the battle is already won. Once this is accepted, the excuse-making has to stop. The will to excel comes from within. High levels of natural achievement are possible if the mind wants it badly enough. Drugs are not necessary and can even be counterproductive, since they wind up limiting the mind by creating a drug dependency. Mental power, properly focused, will allow you to reach your potential in sports.

Goalsetting

Goalsetting is crucial to success. Without the focus that a goal provides, the energy of the mind is scattered like sand in the wind. Goals help you persevere through the tough times, since your efforts are part of a larger picture. The temporary sacrifices are then worth it, because each day brings you closer to the achievement of your goal. This helps you from getting discouraged when you hit sticking points in your training.

It is important to set short-, medium- and long-range goals for your exercise program. It's fine to have a long-term goal of going to the

Olympics, but if you're just starting out in a sport the achievement of that goal may be so far in the future that it winds up depressing you instead of providing inspiration. While it's true that a journey of a thousand miles begins with the first step, you need to focus on the fulfillment of each of those steps rather than spending all your time dreaming about the thrill of victory as they put that gold medal around your neck. Always keep that long-range goal in the back of your mind, however, so you can tap into it when the need arises. Just don't dwell on it to the exclusion of your short- and medium-range goals.

It's been said that it's not enough to want something, you have to plan for it. Truer words were never spoken. A nebulous desire is not sufficiently detailed to charge up the mind with will and energy. You need a specific target to shoot for—something you can clearly see in your mind. Short- and medium-range goals are the means to this end.

These goals need to be realistic so they can help sustain your efforts on a day-to-day basis. Don't bite off more than you can chew. Choose a goal that you have an excellent chance of achieving, say, doing one more repetition on your barbell curls. This goal is modest in the grand scheme of things, yet should be well within your grasp. Go for it and achieve it. Savor the satisfaction that comes from reaching your goal. Feel the thrill of victory, if you will, but don't gloat on your new-found strength. Set another goal for your next workout. Add yet another repetition to your set, or increase the weight by five or 10 pounds. You will build upon your previous successes and reach a medium-range goal, such as winning a local competition. If you can imagine a specific goal in your mind you will be drawn toward it and in time you will achieve it.

Visualization

Visualization is an excellent way to maximize your intensity. Through the use of mental imagery it is possible to achieve a level of concentration and focus that will push you harder than you ever thought possible. Everyone remembers the story of "The Locomotive That Could" from school. Try to create the same level of positive energy and confidence that little locomotive had—I think I can, I know I can, I knew I could! If it helps, imagine yourself going up the same hill as that locomotive, with the peak of the hill being the toughest point in your set—the point where you need maximum intensity to perform the movement. Believe you are a machine, an engine capable of acts of sheer force. By the mechanical laws of nature you *will* achieve your goals! The word failure does not exist. You are the ruler of your destiny, and you *choose* to dominate the weight with your unrestricted will power. Nothing can get in your way!

If you don't find the image of a locomotive too motivating, choose another visualization that works for you. Look through a magazine or book on your sport. Try imagining yourself as one of the drug-free athletes in those photographs. "There I am, in a national magazine. My level of achievement in the sport is so great the photographers took pictures of me!" True, it hasn't happened yet, but one day it will, because your intensity and drive will push your strength and muscular development to the point that you'll stand out from the crowd. All you have to do is perform at 100 percent of your potential on this set, and on this one, and now this one...!

There are as many different visualizations as there are people. Every person who excels in an endeavor, whether it be rising to the top in business or dominating the playing field in a sport, has a clear picture of where he or she wants to get to. This picture should be as detailed as possible, so you can truly believe in the reality of it all.

Think of your visualization as a tree. Some future event, like winning a title or competition, will form the central trunk. To this trunk attach secondary visualizations, which are tied to the main concept like branches on a tree. You could focus on the posing routine that gets you that title, or the events leading up to that race you will win. Attached to these branches are the twigs of smaller visualizations, like dominating the sets of the exercises that will make your posing routine so great that you win that title. Visualize the grand scheme and then divide it into parts. The smaller pieces will help you to believe in your main visualization without getting depressed about the enormity of it all or the distance you still have to travel to reach your main goal.

If you find pictures of the natural champions in your sport to be motivating, try imagining your body as the central trunk, or skeleton, on your tree of visualization. Attach to your skeleton the bodyparts of the athletes you most want to look like. If you feel some bodybuilder has perfectly shaped, incredibly peaked biceps, put those arms on your skeleton. If another muscleman has legs that make the crowd roar when he flexes them, pack those legs onto your skeleton as well. Don't worry about them being from two different people. After all, this is a visualization, and visualization is nothing more than productive fantasy. Form a composite picture of all those bodyparts, and imagine yourself growing day by day in the direction of the picture you have created. Of course, if you find one particular athlete to be perfection personified, you can focus on that one person. The important thing is to dare to dream. Over time the dream and the reality will merge.

Think about these visualizations throughout the day. Let your mind dream about them at night. And most important of all, lock into them when you do your exercises. As you do a bench press, imagine your chest and triceps being transformed into the bodypart of the person you most admire. This positive image increases your intensity and helps you force out that extra repetition or two. Push through your pain barrier and reach new heights of natural strength and sports performance!

You can also use the imagery of the world around you to help you visualize. Rather than focusing on the achievements of another athlete, you could use physical objects as your visualizations. As you train, imagine your biceps becoming mountains of rock-hard muscle—pure granite. Those legs of yours are actually tree trunks, growing slowly but surely on their way to becoming massive red-woods. Some track stars think of themselves as race horses or greyhounds with powerful animal intensity. And most people, of course, want washboard abdominals!

Concentrate on these images as you exercise each bodypart, developing different visualizations for particular muscles if that motivates you more. There's nothing wrong with having granite biceps and steel triceps. You could even alternate the images, one day going for stone-hard arms and the next adding some iron to their structure. The images don't have to "make sense" or be based on reality. That's the great thing about fantasy. So don't start analyzing how realistic the visualizations are. It doesn't matter. You don't have to tell anyone what images you use, and if you don't tell them they won't know. If the visualization is effective, use it. This can truly make the difference between a good athlete and a great athlete.

Some people find they get added training intensity by visualizing a workout in their minds the night before they go to the gym. This should be done in a quiet, comfortable and relaxing setting, such as a peaceful corner of your house or in bed before going to sleep. The mental imagery of going through the steps of a training session can help the mind to focus on the task to come. It may even aid the subconscious in preparing for the next day's lifting. To maximize the effectiveness of this method, all extraneous thoughts have to be pushed out of the mind so it can concentrate on the task at hand.

This can be done in a variety of ways, ranging from meditation to more conventional relaxation techniques. In each case the mind must be emptied of random thoughts and all the static that usually bombards us. Focus on one particular thought and dwell on it until it dominates your entire mind. This thought could be as simple as repeating the word "relax" over and over, or it could be a mantra like those used in Eastern meditation. Concentrating on your breathing may also help, especially if you count to 10 while doing it. Another method is to alternate flexing and relaxing each bodypart, starting with your feet and continuing muscle by muscle until you reach your neck.

Experiment and find the technique that works best for you, then focus on those words, breaths or movements until they become the only things you think about. You'll probably find that thoughts pop into your head even when you don't want to think about them—even thoughts that haven't reached your conscious mind for some time. Don't try to suppress these thoughts. You can't keep the genie in the bottle. Let all of them out so they can escape. Then your mind will be free to concentrate on the important task at hand: tomorrow's workout.

Visualize all of the exercises you will do tomorrow. Imagine yourself achieving the short-term goal you have set for that day. If you have decided to go for an extra 10 pounds on an exercise without reducing the number of repetitions you do, picture the execution of that movement in your mind. Count the reps as you do them. Sure the first few reps are easy, but you keep on going. Five, six, seven—they're getting harder now—but you dominate the weight. Now visualize yourself pumping out that final repetition, straining as you know you must against a piece of iron that seems to get heavier by the instant. But you don't give in. No, you achieve the goal you have set for yourself. Mission accomplished. Now all you have to do is go to the gym and repeat the exercise.

Some natural athletes are able to reach this level of focused concentration in the gym or during competitions. They withdraw from the world around them and enter a lifting trance where their entire consciousness centers on the performance of the exercise. During this trance they block out all of their other feelings and temporarily lose touch with reality. They become one with the movement, resulting in a level of concentration and determination that can make the difference between winning and losing—between reaching their goal for the day and just treading water. To enter a training trance, try locking onto the same thought patterns you focused on the night before. Breath in the same, slow rhythmic way, which should help the trance to "click in." (It may sound difficult, but it gets easier with time.) Your intensity level will rise dramatically.

Variation

One of the secrets to maintaining enthusiasm in weight training is variation. It would get boring to eat the same thing for dinner every night, and an exercise routine is no different. The best way to create excitement and stimulation for your workout is to constantly vary the elements of your natural training program. This fresh approach will increase your intensity level dramatically. Many people have noticed that a new routine, or sometimes even the same routine in the atmosphere of a new gym, will result in greater muscle soreness and growth. Variation is the key to unlocking the power of the mind, and the mind is what determines your strength. Within limits, more variation = greater strength = more goal achievement.

There are many different ways to vary your workout. The number and type of exercises can be changed. Some days you could do three exercises for a bodypart, and on other days two or four. This could mean raising or lowering the number of sets you do of each exercise (so the total number of sets remains constant), or you could have high-volume and low-volume days. Modifying the weights and number of repetitions per set is another option. You could also vary the type of exercises by doing only compound movements with free weights for a while, then switching to machines or isolation movements. Or try concentrating on presses one day and cables the next. Variations in arm and leg positioning can stimulate growth too.

An excellent way to stimulate growth is by systematically programming variation into your routine. This is known technically as periodization. Instead of taking a scattershot approach to varying your training, try structuring the changes in a planned manner. This is frequently done by powerlifters, who start out with high numbers of repetitions at the beginning of their training programs and gradually reduce their repetitions per set as the day of the meet comes closer. Bodybuilders and other drug-free athletes who don't do maximum lifts in competition can use shorter periodizations year round. For six or eight weeks you could do high-repetition exercises with light weight, then switch to low-repetition exercises with heavy weight. Periodization of free-weight exercises with machines is another option. Competitive athletes can also schedule their periodizations to coincide with their contests, timing everything so they reach the event in peak condition.

Experiment with your routine to see which variations work best for you. There is no reason to stick with a group of exercises just because you got some results. Maybe something else will be even more effective. If not, go back to the first workout or try something else. Variety is the spice of life, and there are so many variations in weight training that if you're bored with your routine something's wrong. It could be you're overtraining or something else is amiss. Seek out new options. Explore the possibilities. You'll grow more and have more fun to boot.

Discipline

Discipline is essential to achieving your goals in athletics and life in general. There are always plenty of distractions around and never enough time to do everything you want to do. Being disciplined helps you sift through these difficult choices and establish priorities. This allows you to keep to the goals you have set without impulsive deviations that could take you off course. Once you set a training schedule, you keep to it without skipping days. You follow your diet plan, knowing that overeating now means you'll only have to overdiet later. You choose your path and then stick to it, reaping the rewards in the end.

Discipline also gives you the stamina to persevere through bad times without giving up. There will inevitably be times when you reach sticking points in your training—when nothing seems to progress as rapidly as you would like. A disciplined approach to natural training will keep you on track, helping you overcome periods of moodiness or depression. A journey of a thousand miles, as any disciplined person will tell you, begins with a single step.

Discipline is also required to avoid overtraining. Committed athletes rarely need to be forced into the gym. They enjoy their training—it is one of the high points of their day. Yet their dedication can also hurt them by encouraging them to workout before they are fully recuperated from their last training session. This is especially true for natural athletes, who may try to keep up with the workout programs of drug abusers for fear of being left behind.

Discipline is necessary to make sure that your training regimen is geared to your body's ability to respond and recuperate and not to some impulsive desire of the mind to do everything in sight or to keep up with the Joneses. Natural sports development takes time, but it's infinitely more beneficial and satisfying in the end. Remembering this should give you the discipline to restrict your workouts to the most effective volume of training for you. Discipline your mind to gear the frequency and duration of your workouts to your body's ability to grow in muscle strength or size. That is, after all, what this game is all about!

Balance

A balanced perspective toward your exercise program will give you the greatest rewards. A good sense of balance helps you choose the right combinations of exercises and periodizations and guides your exercise frequency as well, encouraging the right mix of recuperation and training. A balanced approach to life also provides numerous benefits, both in the gym and outside of it. These concepts are discussed more in the chapter **Balancing Your Life**.

Natural bodybuilders need to look at their bodies with a proper sense of balance. One of the most glaring weaknesses that some bodybuilders have is underdeveloped bodyparts. This lack of balance and symmetry reduces the overall aesthetics of the physique and has been responsible for the poor placing of many athletes. Each bodypart should be trained with the same level of intensity. Giving legs lower mental priority will result in less leg development. Saying that your calves won't grow will make it so. Every muscle should receive the same level of attention during training since the entire physique is on display on the posing dais. The only exception would be for a genetically-gifted athlete who had a large bodypart that would grow out of proportion with equal attention. In this case he or she should ease off on this muscle to maintain the proper balance.

If you have a muscle that seems to grow hard, or which is smaller than usual for whatever reason, that bodypart should be trained first during the workout session. For most people, therefore, calves would be trained before quadriceps and hamstrings. If you do your biceps and triceps on the same day, train the weaker bodypart first. This will allow the historic differences between your weaker and stronger muscles to disappear. Of course, you should still do your major compound movements (bench press, deadlift) before your smaller bodyparts (like arms) so you will have maximum strength for your heaviest lifts. You could, however, alternate doing chest and back first if you do them both on the same day. Always strive for balance. The benefits you get in return are many.

Safety

Safety doesn't always make it on a list of natural training principles, yet it is actually fundamental to success in all types of workouts. You can't train while you're injured. In fact, the time off from the gym will cause you to atrophy and lose your strength, so you'll have to start all over again. (Fortunately the gains come back quicker the second time around!) A safe and sound approach to training will ensure that you continue on an upward path toward the achievement of your goals. In the long run this is better than impulsively jumping into something before you are ready—trying to lift too much weight to impress someone, or figuring you can do that heavy squat without a spot. Safety comes first, in this and all things.

Athletes are impulsive go-getters by nature. The concepts of patience and safety do not come easily. We all need to harness our natural energy and enthusiasm so it is channeled into constructive ends and does not self-destruct. By accepting that drug-free athletics allows for only gradual yet longlasting improvement, we can fight off the impulses to do more than it is safe to do on a particular day. This is not to say, of course, that you shouldn't push the edges of your abilities. Total intensity is the only way to grow. Still, a wise athlete knows the fine line between total positive intensity and foolishly going beyond the limit, and stops just short of that line.

Here are a couple of suggestions for injury-free training:

If you have the slightest doubt about your ability to lift a weight, ask a gymmate for a spot. There is nothing negative about realizing you need some assistance and asking for it, especially when it allows you to force out a few more growth-stimulating repetitions. Nearly everyone in a gym will be glad to spot you. They may even ask you to return the favor. So play it safe and ask for help. You many even meet a new friend!

Don't hold your breath while doing an exercise. Sometimes people do this thinking it will help their concentration or power, but the opposite is actually true since the body is deprived of a regular flow of oxygen. The lack of oxygen to the brain, called anoxia, is potentially hazardous. Holding the breath, called the valsalva maneuver, also sets off a series of physical changes that result in temporary high blood pressure and forceful heart contractions, especially with heavy weights. People have even burst blood vessels in their eyes from the high pressure created. The valsalva maneuver places needless stress on your heart muscle—the most important muscle in your body.

Instead of restricting your breathing, use it to your advantage. Think of yourself as a steam engine, and let the forcefulness of your exhaling push your body to new heights of intensity. When you are getting into position for your repetition (going down for a squat or lowering your arms for another biceps curl), breath in. Expand your chest cavity by filling your lungs with air. Then, as you curl or push up for your squat, force the air out quickly like a steam engine would. Become the Locomotive That Could! This will help your intensity level and be a lot safer for you and your heart.

Use proper form on all exercises. Besides assuring maximum use of the muscle you are training and the greatest possible growth stimulation, this is also the safest way to perform the movement. Prevent injuries by lifting and lowering the weights without swinging, and make sure that the poundages are within your current capabilities. This will ensure a safe and successful completion of the lift.

Incorporating the Eight Training Principles into your workout will help you achieve the greatest possible gains for your time and effort. Always keep them in mind when you go to the gym. They are the foundation for all successful drug-free training programs.

CHAPTER TEN
A Natural Exercise Program

While the body needs proper nutrients to operate at its best, improvements in strength and sports performance can only occur as a result of exercise. Exercise forces the body to adapt to the demands of its environment in a very positive way—strengthening the muscles and connective tissues as well as the cardiovascular system. These adaptations move the body to a new and higher level of functioning where it is pushed to its limits and forced to grow.

Exercise allows humans to reach their optimal levels of natural development and sports achievement. It also provides a challenge that can add new dimensions to our lives, producing a number of mental and psychological benefits along with the more visible physical improvements. Pursuing this challenge and eventually reaching the goals we have set for ourselves allows us to savor some of life's best experiences, helping us achieve a full and balanced life.

In this chapter the keys to a successful natural exercise program are discussed. Various suggestions are offered for maximizing your gains from progressive-resistance training. The benefits of warmups, isometric exercise and stretching—three components of a complete workout program which are often overlooked—are also described, as is the need for aerobic conditioning, rest and recuperation. Proper attention to all these interrelated elements will assure you the maximum gains that you are capable of achieving—without drugs.

155

There are many books on the market which promote a single "magic routine." According to these books, all you have to do is follow this one routine and you will be transformed into a modern-day Superhero, packing on 10 or 20 pounds of pure muscle in a matter of weeks. Sometimes these books will tell you to forget everything you have ever heard about other routines. After all, now that you know "the truth," why bother remembering all the other trash you have heard?

There is no such thing as a magic routine. If there were, word would have gotten around by now and everyone would be using it. This is not to say that the routines mentioned in these books are without merit. On the contrary, they have undoubtedly done wonders for their authors and may work for you as well. You just need to have a healthy skepticism for the "miracle workouts" mentioned in the books and magazines.

Every natural athlete is unique, responding to different exercises and workout schedules in his or her own particular way. There is no one perfect routine for everyone. So when you read about a new routine, if it looks interesting, try it out. It probably won't hurt and may indeed stimulate your muscles better than what you were doing before. If so, make it a part of your routine. If not, toss it aside and keep on experimenting. In time you will find the workout program that is most effective for you.

When designing your training routine, beware of the workouts of the "champions" listed in many of the sports magazines and books. It is an unfortunate fact of life that nowadays many of these champs use steroids and/or growth hormone. As a result, their bodies are able to recuperate faster than a natural athlete who doesn't rely on drugs. These drug abusers will therefore be able to do more sets per bodypart every time they work out and train each bodypart more frequently than a natural athlete can. Attempting to copy these routines will certainly get you sore, but you won't grow as much as you would have with the right volume of training.

At the same time, many magazines and books list all of the exercises an athlete ever does for a bodypart. It is not always clear that the athlete selects three or four exercises from this list for a particular workout. Trying to do everything shown in the magazine every time you train is a great way to overtrain, and overtraining is the number-one reason why natural athletes don't reach their goals. So forget about the routines of the drug-users. Determine what exercise frequency is most effective for you and stick with it. You are following the voice of a different drummer. Listen to it and don't get sidetracked by what some professional athlete said he did. Your healthy approach to training will triumph in the end.

WARNING

❖ While exercise can be very beneficial, it can also result in injury—especially if you are not in good physical condition. Always consult with your physician before beginning any program of weight training or exercise. If you start exercising and feel any strain or pain, stop immediately and consult your physician.

❖ Also, remember to follow exercise instructions carefully. Since this book does not deal with the specifics of individual exercises, you are strongly urged to consult other books or a competent personal trainer before performing all exercises. Always start with very light weights and exercise at your own pace. Remember, you can't train and grow if you're injured. Respect your body and it will give you the greatest rewards it is capable of.

Warming Up

Warming up is one of the most important things that you can do to get maximum results from your workout. Many people are in such a rush to begin their exercise routine that they either "forget" to warmup or make excuses that it doesn't really matter. Nothing could be further from the truth. The warmup provides the body with a necessary period of adjustment from the resting state to the active exercise state. Properly performed, it can improve your performance while reducing the chances of injury.

There are many benefits from warming up. The temperature of the body increases, which improves the flow of blood through the muscles to be exercised. There is also an increase in the heart rate, which helps prepare the cardiovascular system for the work to come. Warmups improve the speed at which nerve impulses travel through the body, improving the efficiency of body movement. This allows the muscles to contract and relax with more speed, since these nerve signals can move from the muscle to the brain or spinal cord and vice versa at greater velocities. A warmup increases the rate of certain metabolic processes as well, and facilitates the release of oxygen from the blood.

All of these physiological changes increase the work capacity of the body. The ability of the muscles and connective tissues to stretch and extend themselves improves, while the viscocity (or resistance to movement) within them decreases. This results in a decrease of muscular tenseness and an enhanced potential for performance by the natural athlete. Simply put, warming up readies your body for intense work while it psychs up your mind to charge into the task at hand.

There are three types of warmup: the general body warmup, the bodypart-specific warmup and the exercise-specific warmup. Each has a different role, and all are necessary to be fully warmed up for the high-intensity exercise to come. The general body warmup should be the first thing the natural athlete does at the beginning of a training session. Although this warmup needn't be more than five or 10 minutes long, it will enhance performance throughout the entire workout (provided there are no extended breaks during the training period).

A general warmup, as its name implies, is a period of light exercise. The activity chosen, whether it be stationary biking, speed walking, rowing machine, stair climbing or the like, should be sufficient to raise the heartbeat and breathing rates and cause a bit of perspiration to form. It should not be so intense, however, that it becomes part of your regular workout. There are some compulsive athletes who will do 100 percent intensity on their "warmups," figuring that anything less than that is not worth doing. This misses the entire point of warming up. In fact, such 100 percent exercise is not a warmup at all. You wouldn't think of driving your car on a cold morning without warming it up a bit. So why not give your body—that machine you live in—the same benefit you give your automobile? General warmups prepare the body for performing at its maximum potential and give your mind the time it needs to focus on the coming workout, increasing your total efficiency and intensity. It is five to 10 minutes very well spent.

It is also necessary to warm up each bodypart before beginning high-intensity exercise. The bodypart-specific warmup helps increase the flexibility of the muscles by allowing them to go through their full range of motion at an easy pace before beginning exercise at full-throttle. This movement increases the mobility of the joints as well, fine-tuning the muscle fibers for action and reducing the potential for injury. Bodypart-specific warmups help focus the mind on the specific muscle to be exercised, increasing the internal communication and interaction between mind and muscle. They can also serve as the exercise-specific warmup for the first exercise you do for a particular bodypart.

The final type of warmup is exercise-specific. This warmup allows you to rehearse the actual movement and technique of an exercise before subjecting the muscle to a great deal of resistance. It also allows the body to make minor adjustments in posture, so it can get into proper position for execution of the exercise. This helps prepare the muscle for the heavier weights to come. The exercise-specific warmup should be done using a very light weight. When a great deal of weight is to be lifted eventually, two warmups are often recommended—the second one with a weight approximately halfway between the weight used for the first warmup and the peak weight. This gradual increase in weight is called pyramiding, and is a proven technique for maximum performance and injury prevention.

An exercise-specific warmup should be done for every exercise you do. While some people feel that a warm muscle is entirely warmed up, we have seen that there are many different dimensions to a complete warmup. As a result, you need to fully prime your body for its full-intensity effort. A quick set of eight to 10 repetitions with a light weight can be done in 30 seconds or less. That's a small amount of time to invest for enhancing your natural growth potential.

Progressive Resistance Exercise

Progressive-resistance exercise is a proven way to gain muscular strength and size. By increasing the amount of weight you lift over time, your muscles are forced to adapt to the ever greater work demands you place on them. This brings them to a higher level of functioning, helping you to achieve your sport goals.

When designing a resistance-training program, you need to determine exactly what your goals are. Bodybuilders are most interested in muscle hypertrophy, so their programs are geared toward this one variable. Bodybuilders also need to be concerned with muscle symmetry and proportion, which is crucial to success on the posing dias. This requires strict attention to the relative growth of the individual bodyparts. If one bodypart grows more quickly than another, relatively less time should be spent on the quicker-growing muscle in order to maintain body symmetry. Likewise, slower-developing muscles need to receive relatively more time and attention so they can be brought up to the same size and quality as the other bodyparts.

Deciding how to budget your time to attain perfect symmetry and proportion is one of the more difficult decisions in natural bodybuilding. If you aren't sure about your symmetry, ask a good friend who will give you accurate advise. This attention to detail should start right at the beginning of your training. It is far easier to eliminate a lack of proportion when the muscles are all relatively small than to wait until some muscles are fully developed and others are obviously lagging behind. That takes discipline, of course, but the greatest rewards come to those who are disciplined.

The resistance-training programs for other sports will depend on the event the drug-free athlete is training for and the amount of time he or she has to devote to weight training. Track athletes and bicyclists will be principally interested in increasing their leg power, while athletes who focus on the discus and shotput will concentrate on upper body development. Wrestlers, swimmers and football players will be concerned with full-body strength and endurance.

You should analyze what you want to achieve from your resistance training. Determine whether you are principally interested in training your fast- or slow-twitch muscle fibers (or both), then list your precise training goals and design a program that allows you to reach these goals. This will ensure that your training is directed toward a specific end. It will also allow you to measure your progress toward the goals you have established.

In order to make sure that your training program stays on course, it is highly recommended that you keep track of your performance through some sort of training record. This need not be a fancy notebook, of course. Any old piece of paper will do. The important thing is that you record all of the weights you lift and the number of sets and repetitions you do so you can chart your progress. This will provide you with a guidepost that you can use to select the type of training program that works best for you. By showing how you respond to a particular program, a training record can help you decide whether a new program is better for your purposes than the one you were using previously. A training record is also a valuable motivational tool, since you can see in black and white all of the progress you made with a particular program. This can spur you on to even greater achievements. Without a training record, it is virtually impossible to remember and appreciate all of the subtle improvements that have occurred over time.

In the previous chapter the Eight Training Principles were discussed. These principles should always be kept in mind during your progressive-resistance training. They include the following:

- full range of motion
- intensity
- goalsetting
- visualization
- variation
- discipline
- balance
- safety.

Taken as a whole, these principles lead to an inevitable conclusion: there is no such thing as *the* perfect workout. You need to vary your workouts, both in type and intensity, to achieve maximum progress over time. The best way to do this is by periodization. Every six to eight weeks you should vary your training program. If you've been doing relatively low repetitions (six to eight), try doing higher repetitions (12 to 20) for a while to shock the muscle into responding. After a period of 100 percent intensity, back off a bit to give your body the time it needs to adapt to the new stresses you have placed on it. This will create a new foundation for muscle growth, allowing you to achieve even greater heights in natural sports performance once you return to your 100 percent intensity level. You could also try varying your intensity level on different days of the week, alternating between days of high intensity and low intensity. You could even opt for a three-way schedule of hard, easy and moderate days.

Unless you are in one of the relative relaxation periods just mentioned, always do your sets to failure. Don't stop just because you reach the number of repetitions you originally had in mind. If you can do more, go for it. Push yourself to the maximum. If you were planning on doing eight repetitions for fast-twitch hypertrophy and find that you can do 10, this means that it's time to increase the amount of weight you lift. Raising the weight by five or 10 pounds will lower the number of repetitions you do back to six or seven, but that's fine. Continue at that new weight until you can do more than eight repetitions again, then raise the weight, which will push you back to six or seven repetitions, etc., etc.. Remember that muscles grow as an adaptation to increased resistance. It is essential that you keep on raising the amount of weight you lift (provided that you always maintain good form) so that your muscles are forced to grow in strength and size.

You should also begin lifting your maximum weight just as soon as you are fully warmed up. Sometimes athletes do three or four warmup sets before they reach their maximum weight. One or two of these sets, of course, are necessary to make sure the muscle is completely warmed up and ready for action, especially for leg exercises. Powerlifters who are warming up to do one-repetition maximal lifts will often need to do more than this. Yet for most other athletes any more than two submaximal warmup sets will tire out the muscle needlessly without any benefit in return.

For example, if your goal is to do a set of squats with three 45-pound plates on each side (315 pounds), you should do two warmup sets: one with one 45-pound plate on each side (135 pounds) and another with two plates on each side (225 pounds). This gives your body all the time it needs to warmup. You should then immediately progress to your three-plate squats. Doing a couple of extra sets in between at, say, 250 and 275 pounds is counterproductive, since you will tire yourself out so much on those additional sets that you will not be able to perform at your maximum once you eventually get around to the 315-pound squat. You may not even be able to do 315 pounds after all of those extra sets, even though you would have been able to if it had been the third set you did. So don't burn out by trying to do a lengthy pyramiding scheme to get to your maximum weight. Go for your maximum lift as soon as you are warmed up. That is the way to lift the greatest amount of weight—and that's what progressive resistance is all about.

To achieve the greatest power for your exercises, remember to raise the weight in an explosive movement. These rapid concentric contractions should be done as swiftly as possible while still maintaining good form. Speed is never an excuse for sloppiness. Then, lower the weight relatively slowly to its original position, but never so slowly that you do a prolonged negative movement. As was noted earlier, negatives (eccentric contractions) cause far greater muscle soreness. So forget about doing negatives as part of your workout. Lower the weight slowly enough for you to maintain control of it, then move immediately into the next explosive concentric contraction. This will produce the greatest gains in power with the least amount of muscle soreness.

One of the biggest decisions a natural athlete must make is choosing the frequency and duration of training. These are crucial decisions that only the individual can make based on his or her own experience. Frequency is the number of times you work a bodypart each week. Duration (or volume) is the length of each workout. You need to experiment to see which combination of frequency and duration causes the greatest gains in strength and size.

Sometimes bodybuilders split their routines into three or four separate days so they have time to do 15 to 20 sets per bodypart. Experiment with this system if you like, but you will probably discover that the people who grow from doing fifteen to twenty sets per bodypart are usually on steroids. Try doing fewer sets (less duration) with more frequent training. Remember that your muscles grow from lifting more weight than ever before. If you have done six to eight sets at your maximum weight, there is nothing to be gained by doing another 10 sets at a lower weight. All this will do is tire your muscles so much that it will take them another couple of days to fully recuperate. Maximum weight lifted equals maximum muscle growth. This is not the same as maximum number of sets per day of training, although many people seem to think so. Once you have trained your muscle so hard that it can no longer perform at its maximum, either switch to another bodypart or leave the gym.

Weightlifting is not an endurance sport. It is a peak intensity sport. Your muscles hypertrophy from that one set when you lift more than you ever did before—and not from those 10 sets you did at a weight you have lifted for years. Overtraining your muscles by doing excessive numbers of sets is not the way to achieve maximum muscle strength and size. You have to aim for peak intensity, not muscle burnout. This could well mean doing fewer sets per bodypart than you are used to doing for each workout. It could also mean training more frequently, however, since you will need fewer days off to recuperate from overtraining. So experiment with your training duration and frequency. Finding the right combination can make a major difference.

There is also the question of which exercises to do for each bodypart. Entire books have been written on this subject, and if you want specific information on a particular bodypart or on exercise technique in general, you are encouraged to buy one of these books.

It should be noted, however, that your success as a natural athlete will not be determined by your decision to do a particular exercise for a bodypart. All of the popular exercises "work"—they are all variations on a theme. The important thing is to follow the Eight Training Principles when you do every exercise. This will assure you the greatest possible gains from your progressive-resistance training.

Isometrics

Isometric exercise is an effective yet often-ignored means of gaining strength. Isometrics provide an additional stimulus that the muscles are forced to respond to—over and above that provided by conventional progressive-resistance training. Research has shown that isometrics can produce muscle hypertrophy and strength gains when the isometric contractions are maximal and are performed on a regular basis.

The strength gains from isometric exercise are joint angle specific. That is, the increase in strength is found only within a range of plus or minus 20 percent of the joint angle at which the isometric exercise was performed. This means that for gains in total strength and dynamic power, the isometric exercise should be varied so that the muscle will be worked at many different joint angles. The same specificity principle can also be used to advantage when trying to increase strength at the sticking point—that joint position where a movement is most difficult to perform (that is, where the mechanical advantage for lifting is the smallest). Performing an isometric exercise at this joint angle will allow the drug-free athlete to gain strength at this crucial sticking point, improving his/her performance potential for the entire exercise. This technique is called functional isometrics.

Much of the literature that has been written about isometrics, including the famous Dynamic Tension course by Charles Atlas, promoted isometrics as the sole means of gaining strength. While it does have the advantage of not requiring the use of weights, studies have since proven that, when used alone, isometrics is far less effective than regular weight training for enhancing muscle strength. In fact, rumor has it that even Charles Atlas gained his celebrated physique by occasionally pumping the iron.

However, when used in combination with progressive-resistance training, isometrics can have significant value by giving you a supplemental means of developing strength naturally. Wrestlers will find this isometric strength especially helpful, since many of their holds are isometric in nature. So try an experiment and add some isometrics to your routine immediately after performing some of your sets with weights.

Without holding your breath, maintain isometric tension for 15-20 seconds or to failure. When tension is applied to the already exhausted muscle an additional growth stimulus is provided. It's sort of like doing forced reps but without the weight. The best way to do an effective isometric exercise is to flex the bodypart. This does not mean promenading in front of the mirror for all to see. It is just as effective to do the flexing movement while seated on a bench nonchalantly "waiting" to do your next set.

Since most people take at least 60 seconds between their sets, this isometric movement basically occupies dead time and puts it to good use. It therefore makes the exercise a kind of superset without moving between (and trying to save) two pieces of equipment. Also, once you get the feel of the isometric movement you will be able to perform it in an inconspicuous manner that will not arouse attention. So try adding some isometrics to your weight-training program. You may well find that your strength increases faster than it would have with the weights alone. And since greater strength allows the muscle to lift more weight, greater hypertrophy and muscle mass will be the welcome result.

Bodybuilders have also found that isometric flexing improves their muscular detail and vascularity. This is one of the reasons why they practice their posing so much before a competition. It is still unknown, however, why these physical changes occur.

Stretching

Stretching is a vital part of a complete workout. Stretching is usually considered to be a flexibility movement, and, of course, it does make the body more flexible. However, stretching can also enhance athletic skills like agility and coordination, which is particularly important in sports like gymnastics and karate. It can reduce stress through the relaxation of the muscle and help prevent injury to the joints and tendons. Properly done, it can also relieve muscle soreness and increase muscular strength.

A slow non-bouncing stretch, called a static stretch, has been shown to reduce immediate muscle soreness. Everyone is familiar with the use of a stretch to relieve a muscle cramp. Research has now shown that static stretching decreases the electrical activity within skeletal muscle, which may explain why it is effective for soreness. Care must be taken, however, to use the correct stretching technique. When performing a stretch, don't force the muscle to tense up by straining it. The whole point of stretching is to release tension, allowing the muscle fibers (and all those sarcomeres) to elongate.

Visualize the muscle expanding like an elastic band. Keep on lengthening the fibers slowly and without stress. If you feel a burning sensation or if the muscles begin to quiver you have gone too far, possibly to the point where additional tearing of the muscle fiber (and delayed onset muscle soreness) occurs. Ease off a bit. The purpose of stretching is to increase the potential length of your muscles—not to shock them with pain. Of course, over time your muscles will adapt to these movements and become more flexible, allowing you to stretch them further without getting a pain sensation.

Done correctly, stretching can extend your muscles' effective range of motion. A muscle moves through only a portion of its total range during everyday life, so there is a significant reserve capacity. In weight training, however, we want to move the resistance through the fullest range of motion the muscle is capable of. Since stretching allows you to move through a greater portion of this range, it allows the muscle to perform a longer and more complete movement, requiring the myofilaments in each sarcomere to contract over a greater distance than they otherwise would have. Greater forces are therefore produced, stimulating additional muscular adaptations.

To be most effective in producing natural muscle growth, the stretch should be done immediately before the muscle contraction. This is due to the stretch reflex which, like any reflex action, causes a reaction to the initial movement. Prestretching a muscle activates certain nerve impulses in the muscle spindles that set this reflex action into motion. The end result is a stronger contraction and a greater total amount of generated tension, which induces more hypertrophy in the trained muscle. Taking the time to stretch, therefore, is a very wise investment. And since the stretch can usually be done during the rest period between sets, no training time is actually lost. Try it and see.

Aerobics

Aerobics is a necessary part of a balanced training program. Some strength athletes feel that aerobics destroys muscle tissue and should therefore be cut out of their routines entirely so they can concentrate on their weightlifting. This approach, however, overlooks several important points. Aerobic conditioning provides major benefits which cannot be obtained from resistance training. Aerobic activity strengthens the cardiovascular system by forcing the heart to work at a rate less than its maximum (submaximal effort) for a longer period of time than weight training allows. Aerobics help burn the free fatty acids in the body as well, resulting in a more defined, muscular appearance. Moderate amounts of aerobic activity can also stimulate the conversion of lactic acid back into pyruvic acid and glucose, which reduces short-term muscle soreness.

As was mentioned in the **Muscular Development** chapter, there are two major sources of energy for exercise: anaerobic and aerobic. The anaerobic system produces energy without oxygen, while the aerobic system needs oxygen to provide energy. Anaerobic energy is the type predominantly used for progressive-resistance training. Aerobic activity, on the other hand, uses oxygen. This is important because the fatty acids in the body can only be "burned" in the presence of oxygen. Therefore, the only way you can get rid of your body fat through exercise is to add aerobics to your workout. As a result, you should always include some aerobics in your weekly training program. One to 1 1/2 hours of aerobics per week is all you need to keep your cardiovascular system in good working order.

Natural athletes who are getting ready for a competition that requires making a weight class or having minimum body fat levels may want to spend more time at aerobics to meet their weight or fat reduction goals. This aerobic conditioning should consist of two or three half-hour to 45-minute sessions. Be sure to do at least a half-hour of aerobics at any one time because it takes a while for the body to switch into aerobic metabolism. Too short of an exercise session will therefore not provide you with the desired benefits. Always remember to include a five-minute warmup and a five-minute cooldown with your aerobics as well as a bit of stretching. This will ensure a well-rounded natural exercise program for all the reasons mentioned earlier. Don't count this time as part of your minimum half-hour, however.

Also, pace yourself so your aerobics are as beneficial as possible. Try to do your aerobic activity at an intensity level that is from 60 to 80 percent of your maximum heart rate. This aerobic training range, which is illustrated in Figure 2, is the most effective for aerobic (and fat) metabolism. Much more than 80 percent will bring the anaerobic energy systems back into play, and anything less than 60 percent will be so low that you'll need to spend a lot longer exercising to burn the fat you want to get rid of. It's also less exercise for your heart. To determine your maximum heart rate per minute, subtract your age from 220. (Your maximum rate declines with age.) Then multiply that rate by 60 and 80 percent to determine your desired range of heart beats. You can measure your heart rate by taking your pulse manually or with one of the machines now on the market.

Make it a point to vary the aerobic activities you do. The body is a very efficient system, and it responds to changes in its environment by adapting to the demands placed on it. Simply put, if all you do is jog for aerobics, your body will get very efficient at that activity. This is a great way to conserve energy, but nowadays most people are more concerned with limiting their body-fat levels. The more efficient you are in producing energy for jogging, the less fat you will burn. As a result, you should do a variety of aerobic exercises such as stationary or outdoor bicycling, rowing machine, skiing machine, stair climbing or powerwalking. Think of this variation as a form of periodization. Besides fooling your system into burning more fat, your aerobic training will be a lot more interesting than it would have been doing the same thing all the time.

Sometimes natural athletes hear that aerobics should be cut out of their training programs so their muscle fibers will not become overtrained. Yet by and large, different types of muscle fibers are called into use for aerobics and resistance training respectively. As was noted earlier, there are two main types of muscle fibers: slow-twitch and fast-twitch. Slow-twitch fibers have a slow speed of contraction and are fatigue resistant. It is this type of fiber that is used almost exclusively for sustained submaximal activities like aerobics. Also, when the brain sends a contraction signal to the muscle, that message goes to a motor unit, which is a cluster of muscle fibers connected to a nerve. All the fibers in a particular motor unit are of the same type. As a result, the brain selectively directs its electrical impulses to fast- or slow-twitch fibers, depending on the activity involved.

Therefore, aerobics and resistance training are complementary parts of a natural exercise program. Both should be included to ensure your long-term physical health. While some studies have shown that excessive aerobics can hurt an athlete's strength development, the consensus is that one to 1 1/2 hours per week does not have any negative impact on strength. Just be sure that you're eating enough carbohydrates, since both types of activity use muscle glycogen to varying degrees for fuel. Provided you supply your muscles with enough glycogen, however, there is no reason that a moderate level of aerobics will harm your weight-training progress. And your heart will be thankful for the additional stimulation.

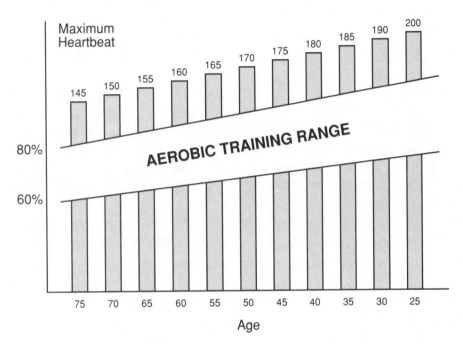

Figure 2 - Aerobics Training Range

Rest and Recuperation

Athletes enjoy their training. Going to the gym is one of the highlights of their day—a time when they can make progress toward their goal of getting bigger and stronger. Taking time off is considered a negative. "No pain, no gain" they're told. "You can't grow sitting on a couch wishing it would happen." Our society constantly reinforces this mentality with its more-is-better philosophy. "If some training is good, more training must be better. You can't have too much of a good thing!" Natural athletes are confronted with this message continually. Every month a barrage of magazine articles appears on professional athletes who do marathon training sessions six times a week and grow. "If it works for them, it'll work for me," the natural athlete reasons. "All I have to do is train like the pros, and one day I'll be a pro!"

Unfortunately, that's not the way it works. It is a sad fact of life that many of the professional athletes nowadays are on steroids. As a result, their bodies can temporarily recuperate faster than someone who pursues the natural route to athletic excellence. If you try to keep up with the training programs of the drug-dependent pros you will overtrain. And since your body will not have the time it needs to recuperate fully, you will not progress in your athletic development. When it comes to building your body there *is* such a thing as too much.

Only you can determine the frequency and duration of training that is right for you. No one system works for everyone because individual bodies vary. There are individual differences as well in the stress levels produced by work and emotional relationships. This stress often prolongs the recuperation process. Of course, it is essential to get the raw materials your body needs for muscular growth from proper nutrition. However, proper nutrition is not enough. You can eat all the protein you want and get plenty of vitamins and minerals, but without adequate rest and recuperation you will never grow.

Always train at your peak intensity. Just checking in at the gym and going through the motions with the same weight and same number of repetitions you always do will get you nowhere, since your body will just be repeating something it has done before. It's better to take a day off (or two days if necessary) and fully recuperate so you can lift more weight than ever before. *That* will make you grow.

The fundamental difference between running a marathon and the weight sports like bodybuilding or powerlifting is that a marathon requires a submaximal effort for a long period of time, while the weight sports demand a maximal effort for a short period of time. If you can't give it your all when you go to the gym, you're better off not going. Forcing yourself to work out when your body is giving you subtle hints that it wants a day off will not produce the results you want.

If you train at peak intensity your muscles will be mildly sore for a day or two after you exercise them. (Not like that intense soreness you felt when you started training, however.) If the muscles aren't sore at all, you haven't pushed yourself hard enough. You may just be going through the motions at the gym. Examine your mental approach to training and see how you can increase your intensity level. Check the poundages you use to see if you've increased them lately. It may be that the amount of weight you're lifting has stabilized without your realizing it. If so, increase the weights you use. You could also boost the number of repetitions you do on each set. Better yet, try doing both.

While muscle soreness is not a direct factor in muscular growth it is an indication that you have trained the muscle hard enough to cause the adaptations needed for hypertrophy. In this sense, some soreness is good. If you're constantly sore, however, you're getting too much of a good thing. Soreness, as was mentioned earlier, results from microtears in the muscle fibers. This damage at the cellular level is repaired as the muscle grows. However, if you exercise so much that your body is always sore, you never give your muscles the time they need to recuperate and grow.

Here's a good rule to follow for optimal recuperation: never exercise a bodypart until it has been free from soreness for at least a day. If you find that applying this rule gets in the way of your current workout schedule, try one of two things: stretch out your training schedule or reduce the number of sets you do per bodypart at each workout. Some drug-free bodybuilders have changed from the traditional three-day division of bodyparts to a four-day division. Others have added a day or two of rest between every exercise cycle. Both of these variations lengthen the period between training sessions for a particular bodypart and increase the time available for recuperation.

Another option is to cut down on the number of sets for each bodypart. This way there is less stress on the muscle from each exercise session and less time needed for recovery. Remember that the muscle grows from peak intensity—not an excess volume of training. If you lift a few sets at your maximum weight and then find that the weights you use keep dropping and dropping, you're better off stopping your bodypart workout right there. You're not going to grow from a few more sets at lighter weight. On the contrary, these extra sets will just increase the stress on your muscle and lengthen the period of necessary recovery. So try experimenting with the number of sets to see how your muscles recuperate. You may well find they grow more with fewer sets.

Rest is a vital part of natural recuperation. The body requires rest to perform at its best. This includes adequate sleep and enough relaxation time during the awake hours to bring about a state of physical and mental refreshment. Many of the benefits derived from sleep actually occur in the first few hours. It is during this period that most people fall into a deep sleep and the repair process operates at full speed. The greatest release of growth hormone also takes place during these first few hours of sleep.

Different people have different sleep requirements. Some people get along on as little as five or six hours, while others require at least eight. The reasons for this individual variation are still not known, although metabolism seems to be partly responsible. Weight training can increase the amount of sleep required as the body works to fully recuperate before the next exercise session. If too much additional sleep is required, however, the body may well be signaling you that you are overtraining. This may result in sleeping through a radio alarm that normally would wake you up and other abnormalities. Overtraining can also reduce the quality of sleep by disturbing sleep patterns and even waking the athlete up during the night. If your muscles are so sore that you wake up every time you move in bed, this will also reduce the effectiveness of your sleeping hours.

As a rule you should not sleep more than eight hours a day—nine at the very most. After seven hours the heartbeat reaches its basal rate. This lowers the metabolism and makes your blood circulation sluggish. At the same time your muscles begin to lose their tone. The longer you stay in bed the more time your body has to slow down. This reduces the number of calories you burn and can even make you weaker. More than eight hours of sleep will not give you additional energy, either.

The body cannot store sleep and it can't catch up on lost sleep either. Therefore, it is essential to get the sleep you need every night. You can't spend Saturday night out on the town and wake up at your usual time, figuring that you'll catch up on that sleep during the week. It doesn't work that way. The body also seems to perform at its best when sleep takes place at roughly the same time every day. This provides a continuity that the body thrives on. Factory workers on rotating shifts have often noticed how the quality of their sleep is effected by radical changes in the times of day they rest, even when the actual number of hours slept remains the same. Natural athletes should try to minimize these shifts in sleep patterns. This will allow the body's recuperation and muscle development systems to operate at peak efficiency, ensuring them maximum benefit for all of their hard work.

A Final Note

This chapter has discussed the essential components of a natural exercise program, ranging from warmups to proper rest and recuperation. The importance of a balanced approach to exercise has been noted, as has the need for warmups, isometrics and stretching in addition to conventional resistance training. Proper use of these techniques will assure you the greatest possible gains you are capable of—provided that you believe in yourself.

Confidence in your eventual success is crucial in rising to the top of any sport. You need to visualize success and believe with all your heart that someday you will achieve your goals. Create a picture in your mind of the future you that is as vivid as possible. Harness your feelings and desires, and channel your energy into the implementation of your dreams. Since experiencing success is the key to self-confidence, show yourself that you can be successful by setting small achievable goals and doing all that is necessary to make them happen. Once you have felt this feeling of success, your confidence will rise, and you will be ready to take on even bigger challenges. So create these new habits of thinking and doing that will bring you the success you seek. I'm sure you'll find you will achieve your goals without resorting to drugs. And the long-lasting results of your self-confidence will be visible for all to see.

CHAPTER ELEVEN

Balancing Your Life

Throughout this book you have seen the different ways you can maximize your potential as a natural athlete. The individual variations in muscle physiology were noted, as were the roles these play in promoting muscular development. The importance of diet and nutrition was discussed as well, along with specific exercise techniques you can use to stimulate your body in the most efficient way, assuring you the gains you seek. All of these elements work together to create the optimal conditions for body growth and development, regardless of the sport you wish to excel in. There is, however, one final element that is needed to bring it all together: the concept of balance.

The Need for Balance

Balance isn't one of those niceties of life that sound good but don't really mean much. On the contrary, balanced athletes can outperform athletes who have let their lives get out of kilter. It allows them to focus with greater intensity on the task at hand and achieve the greatest performance they are capable of. From this viewpoint, balance is something that is essential to achieving your goals naturally.

Balance exists when the physical and mental aspects of life are in sync. Training does not dominate your life, nor is it dominated by your work or other forms of play. There is variety, with a career and social activities each adding to the total enjoyment in life. Even within the training regimen, routines are balanced between resistance training and aerobics, between indoor activities and outdoor ones. There is also a balance between exercise and recuperation, and even between dietary strictness and that little splurge that gives you an emotional boost. Balance allows you to reach your greatest potential as a natural athlete and as a person, soaring to the heights of your goals and dreams. You can then get the greatest satisfaction from your achievements, since you have the perspective to appreciate your accomplishments in a healthy way.

"Balance sounds great," you might say, "but how can I achieve it? I'd love to have a balance between training and work—try to convince my boss! All he wants is to drain the energy out of me. If only I had the time! There are only so many hours in the day and more than enough ways to spend them enjoyably." Very true. Yet it isn't necessary to spend an equal number of hours at two activities for them to be in balance. A four-hour work day would be considered underworking by most people (certainly your boss!), but a four-hour training session would be overkill, even for an athlete on drugs, much less a natural athlete.

Anything in excess can be hazardous to a person's psychological or physical health in the long run. Also, anything in excess will eventually get boring, as the person tires of his or her routine. The way to enhance long-term productivity is to maintain a healthy balance in life.

For example, some of the bodybuilders with the greatest longevity in their sport have had outside interests. Bill Pearl, who competed for many years and still remains active in the sport, has an antique car collection. John Grimek, Mr. America in 1940 and 1941, is a fan of the opera. Of course, you may not be into cars or soprano solos, but there is some interest you do have, even if you haven't developed it yet as a hobby or personal activity. Try spending the time to expand it into a significant part of your life. You may find that, far from reducing your commitment and achievement in your sport, it will actually help your training by giving you another outlet for your energies. This should allow you to focus more fully on your training during the times when it *is* the primary activity, since it will be a variation from the other aspects of your life.

There are several signs which tell when life is in balance. There are greater feelings of self-contentment and a healthier orientation toward life. Outlooks become more long-term, and you become more objective about the inevitable ups and downs of life. Balance also leads to greater efficiency and productivity in work. The person is able to focus 100 percent of their energies on the task at hand without the distractive daydreaming and poor mental focus that can come from an overdose of work or even training.

When it comes to choosing a balance in physical activities, try spending time at a variety of sports or interests. A powerlifter, for example, might occasionally try some rock climbing or mountain biking or even canoeing or river rafting. Some people might say that these "diversions" would hold the natural athlete back from his or her powerlifting goals, but such balance in physical activities can actually help. Since there is more diversity in life there will be a lot more mental stimulation. And since mental focus is at least 80 percent of any sport, the increase in stimulation will lead to a greater level of achievement on the lifting platform, the track or the posing dais. These outside activities are therefore body-building, in its larger sense.

If training starts to become drudgery or "work" in the usual sense, don't give up! Examine the reasons for this change in mood. It may well be due to a lack of balance. Try seeking out new activities to complement the onesidedness of your current routine. Often, an activity that takes only a couple of hours per week can create a better sense of balance. Some people get it from meditation! It needn't affect the amount of time you spend training at all. Yet the results of this balance should become evident in your performance right away.

One of the best ways to achieve balance is by having an active social life. Spending time with friends, neighbors or loved ones does not keep you from succeeding in your career or your sport. On the contrary, the time spent in the company of others lightens the burden of your work, allowing you to share experiences with those around you. The relaxation that comes from socializing also helps the recuperation process and spurs you on to greater achievement. Most importantly, however, a social life brings you closer to other people and makes you a part of their lives. This interaction enriches everyone's experience, especially yours.

A balanced outlook leads to a greater acceptance of the way things are now, along with a greater sense of power to change things in the future. Chances are that as an athlete you are not satisfied with your current level of achievement in your sport. Sure, you might run faster, lift more or have bigger biceps than most people, but that is not enough for you. You want to be on top! That motivation leads you to strive to achieve your goals and to sacrifice and train as hard as you can to reach them. Yet progress takes time, especially when you're natural. Without a balanced perspective, natural athletes can get caught up in a cycle of despair that actually hinders progress in their sport.

Anyone who has tried to excel in sports knows that progress is not a straight, upward line. There are good days and bad days. Two steps forward and then one back. Nothing can be more frustrating than to fail attempting to do something you did just a day or a week before. A squat that was almost easy the last time you trained now requires help on the very first repetition! This is nothing to get depressed about. If the long-term trend is upward, the direction is positive and something to take great satisfaction in. If the direction is only level or negative, your training may be out of balance with the rest of your life. You may not be recuperating enough or your diet may be deficient in some way. Analyze the reasons for this and look for a balanced solution.

The Left-Brain and the Right-Brain

Every individual is a complex combination of emotions and tendencies. We all have two halves in our brains, the left-brain and the right-brain, which can give us different and sometimes conflicting messages. The left-brain is concerned with the intellectual aspects of life. It deals with scientific reasoning and efficiency. Order and reason are its rallying calls and it uses facts to analyze and master its world. The right-brain, on the other hand, is more centered on emotion. Here are the creative and intuitive elements of reasoning, where feelings and emotions rule. Inspiration and imagination are prized, and play is valued.

Every individual gives a different priority to the thoughts coming from both parts of his or her brain. This is what makes each of us unique. It is important, however, to try to balance these tendencies so that the optimal athletic development can be achieved.

Left-brained people tend to be very precise in their training, following strict rules and procedures to guide them on their way. They probably keep to a strict diet and use food scales to count their calories. Since they want to dominate their bodies, training is serious, intense work for them. They try to develop a routine based on the best research they can dig up and then stick to it religiously. Being rational, they establish long- and short-term goals, and move toward them with mechanical precision. They likely use a tape measure, scale or stop-watch to measure their progress. Left-brained athletes may get satisfaction from the achievement of their goals, but are likely to set a new goal just as soon as they accomplish the last one. They are driven to be achievers and strive for perfection.

Right-brained people, on the other hand, tend to be more instinctive with their training. Rather than sticking to a set routine, they seek variety to add to the emotional benefits of training. They experiment with different equipment and training techniques so that no two routines are alike. Each workout takes them into new feelings and experiences. Training is fun, because if it weren't they wouldn't do it. They like to break the rules, try new things and purposely do them differently from the way "everyone else" does them. As far as diet goes, they tend to avoid scales and mechanical devices, going by feel or by the look in the mirror to measure their progress. There may also be a preference for outdoor activities, particularly when it comes to aerobics. The bike ride along the beach is favored over the mechanical precision of the stationary bike. Intuition guides them when it comes to training times, frequency of training and rest periods. The right-brained athlete also experiences pleasure and positive emotion in achieving gains in his/her sport. The amount of this pleasure is the criterium by which progress is evaluated.

Of course, no natural athlete is totally left-brained or right-brained. We all have both halves and make greater use of one half depending on our particular upbringing and nature. Each half of the brain has something to say for it. Rationality can result in more goal achievement than empty dreaming can ever provide. At the same time, bringing the emotional and intuitive part of the brain into the training process may reduce overtraining and result in greater, more pleasurable gains. We need to be aware of these divergent tendencies within all of us and try to form a balanced outlook toward our training and participation in sports.

This balanced outlook also eliminates the need for steroids in sports. Steroid use usually comes from an emotional desire to get results quicker than a natural athlete can achieve. This is a result of a right-brained desire for immediate experience—an emotional demand for gratification that doesn't want to wait the time it takes for a step-by-step, goal-oriented, left-brained approach toward sports achievement. A balanced long-term approach toward athletic progress would stop drug abuse dead in its tracks. Drugs would become superfluous. They would be recognized as counterproductive to realizing your *long-term* potential as an athlete.

Everyone has his or her own particular routines, both in athletic training and in everyday life. Routine can be a valuable way to achieve your goals, since by sticking to a series of activities (provided they make sense from a technical point of view) you can reach the objectives you have established. Maintaining continuity in your training pattern also allows you to do small experiments with specific variables. For example, if you keep your training routine the same (in terms of sets, repetitions, etc.) and change your diet, you will be able to isolate the effects of those dietary variations and decide whether to include them in your permanent training program. If you didn't have a routine, it would be impossible to determine what caused what.

A balanced approach toward routine is required, however. Routines can be a trap, especially if the person is not open to the need for change in certain circumstances. If you have been following the same routine for six months and nothing has changed in terms of weights lifted or speed per mile, your routine may be keeping you from advancing in your performance. Look for new approaches. Modifying a single variable may be all that is needed. Blind adherence to routine can actually result in lost opportunities for progress.

The Three Personality Types

There are three main personality types when it comes to training: the impulsive trainers, the hesitators and the balanced trainers. The impulsive and hesitator types form the two ends of the spectrum, with the balanced trainers in the middle. It is, of course, the balanced individuals who receive the greatest benefits and sense of achievement in their sport.

Impulsive individuals are so gung-ho that they overdo most everything they attempt. For instance, impulsive weight trainers will launch into their full-intensity workouts without a warmup (why waste the time?) and then use weights that are so heavy they can't perform the exercises correctly. They likely do too many sets of too many exercises, resulting in overtraining. They are prone to guilt trips about their training intensity and work out too frequently without adequate recuperation. They may even rush between sets and exercises in an attempt to be as "intense" as possible.

These personality traits can lead to less than optimal gains and even injury. Impulsive individuals tend to ignore pain as a sign of danger, feeling that they can "work through the pain." They fail to see the difference between the positive muscle soreness you get when you overload a muscle and the negative pain sensation that comes with excessive exertion or injury. While it may seem that these people are disciplined athletes, they are actually so impulsively driven to train that they risk injury from their lack of caution. They set goals that are unrealistic and then put their personal health at risk just so they can accomplish them. These self-destructive tendencies keep impulsive athletes from maximizing the gains from all their hard work.

Hesitators, on the other hand, go through the motions of working out without ever reaching sufficient intensity to make gains in their sport. Afraid of discomfort and pain, these persons shy away from the sustained and intense effort that is needed for top performance. They rarely experience muscle soreness. Hesitators lack real discipline. They may force themselves to go to the gym out of some sense of obligation, only to pass the time doing too few sets at too light a weight for it to make any difference. They may spend a lot of time talking between sets. This type of person is likely to have a level of muscular development that is less than one might expect for the number of years they have been exercising. They hold back from the effort needed to achieve. Paradoxically, it is sometimes those people who fear injury the most that wind up getting injured, since they do not put their full concentration into the execution of an exercise and therefore subconsciously invite mishaps. Their voices may say one thing but their actions say another.

Both the impulsive trainers and the hesitators hold themselves back in their natural athletic development due to an unbalanced approach to their sport. By operating at the extreme ends of the spectrum they do not allow their bodies to benefit from all the time and effort they put into their training. For the impulsive individuals, less volume of exercise and a more balanced approach to training in their life would likely result in greater gains by reducing the overtraining that is holding them back. The hesitators would benefit from the greater mental focus and intensity that balance provides, allowing them to get more advantage from their workouts. This would be true even if the volume of time spent at the gym decreased, as long as the former hesitators put 100 percent effort into their exercises when they did train.

Achievement is one of the greatest feelings around. To set a goal and then achieve it brings a satisfaction that few things in life can match. A balanced training program allows you to capture these feelings as often as possible. Your respect for the limits of your body and the dangers inherent in your sport leads you to an awareness of potential problems. You exercise care and caution in your workouts, aiming for the maximum possible training intensity you can achieve without overtraining or undertraining. The sensitivity to your body's needs and signals helps you to back off when needed, avoiding injury. You respect the inevitable ups and downs that come with athletic training and accept these as part of the process.

Most importantly, your workouts are fun. You make the most of them because your balanced approach to sport keeps them from becoming drudgery. You become more in touch with your body. You experience the pleasure that comes from physical activity—the excitement that comes from seeing your body change and improve.

So go out there and make your mark in your sport! Experience the thrill of victory, and maybe even the temporary agony of defeat, but savor the emotions. Go beyond the usual and the mundane and take the risks that all natural achievers must take to rise to the top. You now know that steroids need not be a part of the winning equation. You have learned the ways you can manipulate your body naturally through diet, nutrition and exercise to accomplish your goals. Now it's up to you. If you are committed, you will achieve. I wish you all the luck in the world.

Index